AN INTRODUCTION TO

COLLEGE GEOMETRY

THE MACMILLAN COMPANY
NEW YORK · BOSTON · CHICAGO
DALLAS · ATLANTA · SAN FRANCISCO

MACMILLAN AND CO., LIMITED
LONDON · BOMBAY · CALCUTTA
MADRAS · MELBOURNE

THE MACMILLAN COMPANY
OF CANADA, LIMITED
TORONTO

AN INTRODUCTION TO

COLLEGE
GEOMETRY

by E. H. TAYLOR, PH.D.
PROFESSOR OF MATHEMATICS, EMERITUS
EASTERN ILLINOIS STATE COLLEGE

and G. C. BARTOO, A.M.
PROFESSOR OF MATHEMATICS, EMERITUS
WESTERN MICHIGAN COLLEGE OF EDUCATION

NEW YORK · 1949

THE MACMILLAN COMPANY

LEWIS-CLARK NORMAL SCHOOL
LEWISTON, IDAHO

Printed in the United States of America

Preface

This text is designed especially to meet the needs of the following classes of students:

For students who have mathematics as a major or a minor subject this book provides an introduction to the ideas and methods of modern geometry needed for advanced study.

For prospective teachers of secondary mathematics the book provides an extension of Euclidean geometry to theorems not usually included in present secondary school courses, special attention to methods of proof, a broadening of the base of knowledge of geometry by an introduction to modern ideas and methods, and suggestions for stimulating students' interest in geometry by references to its history and development.

For students who are interested in geometry as a field of human knowledge the authors hope that the presentation will stimulate a desire for further study and will suggest some of the charm that has existed in the logical development of geometry since the days of the ancient Greeks.

The treatment here given assumes only such knowledge of geometry as may come from a year's course in plane geometry in a high school.

An attempt has been made to make the presentation such that it can be read and mastered by the student. The exercises are graded so that every student with a fair mastery of the text can do many of them, but some will challenge the efforts of the best students.

In this revision the historical notes have been expanded and new material has been added, the lists of exercises have been carefully revised, and minor changes have been made in the proofs of theorems for purposes of clarity.

The authors wish to express their acknowledgment to Dean Hobart F. Heller, Eastern Illinois State College, and Dr. Charles Butler, Western Michigan College of Education for suggestions and assistance in making this revision.

E.H.T.
G.C.B.

Contents

CHAPTER 1 Directed Lines and Angles

Directed Lines. A line may be considered as the path of a moving point. It is often useful and convenient to consider the direction in which a point moves in tracing an indefinite line or in tracing a *line segment*, by which we mean that part of the line between two fixed points.

If in Figure 1 the point that traces the segment moves from A to B, the segment is denoted by AB; if it moves from B to A, the

A —————————————————————————— B

Figure 1

segment is denoted by BA. If one direction, as from A to B, is considered positive, the other direction, from B to A, is considered negative.

Segments traced to the right are usually considered positive and those traced to the left negative.

In Figure 1, AB is considered positive and BA negative, therefore $AB = -BA$.

In the segment AB, A is called the *initial point* and B the *terminal point*. If the segment in Figure 1 is read BA, then B is the initial point and A is the terminal point.

Measurement. *To measure* a magnitude is to find how many times it contains another magnitude of the same kind called *the unit of measure.*

1

The number of times a magnitude contains a given unit of measure is called its *numerical measure* with respect to that unit.

For example, if we say a line segment is 10 feet long the numerical measure of the line segment is *10* with respect to the unit of measure *1 foot.*

We shall assume that every line segment may be measured and hence that to every line segment there corresponds a number, and that the operations of algebra may be performed upon line segments the same as upon numbers.

Addition of Line Segments.   To *add* the segment CD to the segment AB place AB on the indefinite line XY. Then, without

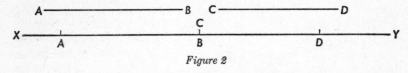

Figure 2

changing the direction of CD, place the initial point C of CD on the terminal point B of AB and make D fall on XY.   The segment from the initial point of AB (A) to the terminal point of CD (D) is the *sum* of AB and CD.   That is, $AB + CD = AD$.

To add the segment DC to the segment AB place AB on the indefinite line XY.   Then without changing the direction of DC

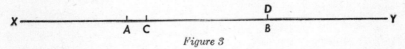

Figure 3

place the initial point D of DC on the terminal point B of AB and make C fall on XY.   Thus $AB + DC = AC$.   It is evident that $AB + DC = AB - CD$.   The subtraction of one line segment from another is but a special case of addition.

Ratio of Line Segments.   The *ratio* of one magnitude to another of the same kind is the quotient of the first divided by the second.

To find the ratio of a first magnitude to a second, then, is to measure the first by the second taken as the unit of measure.

The ratio of two magnitudes is the same as the ratio of their numerical measures. For if u is the unit of measure, and A contains u, m times and B contains u, n times, then $A = mu$ and $B = nu$ and

$$\frac{A}{B} = \frac{mu}{nu} = \frac{m}{n}.$$

We shall frequently refer to the ratio of line segments without assuming that their numerical measures have been found.

Incommensurables. The attempt to measure a line segment by any segment chosen at random as the unit leads at once to incommensurables. Two line segments are said to be *incommensurable* if there exists no unit of measure which is contained in each segment an integral number of times. For example, the side and the diagonal of a square are incommensurable.

The discovery of this fact greatly disturbed the Pythagoreans and stimulated them to make many important discoveries in geometry.

EXERCISES

1. What is the ratio of a side of a square to its diagonal?
2. What is the ratio of a circle to its radius?

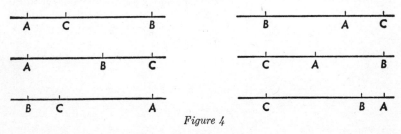

Figure 4

3. In Figure 4 are shown the six possible arrangements of three distinct points on a line. Show in each case that $AC + CB = AB$.
4. In Figure 4, since $-BC = CB$, show in each of the six arrangements that $AC - BC = AB$.

Use Figure 5 to find these results:

5. $AB + BC + CD + DA = 0.$ 7. $DA + AB =$
6. $AC + CB =$ 8. $DA + AB + BC =$

 9. $AC + CA =$ 12. $AC - BC =$
10. $DC + CB + BA =$ 13. $DA - BA =$
11. $BC + CA =$ 14. $DA - BA - CB =$

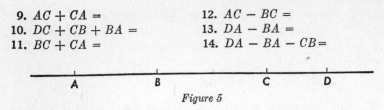

Figure 5

Directed Angles.   An angle may be thought of as being generated
by rotating a line about a fixed point on it from one position, the
initial side, to another position, the *terminal* side.

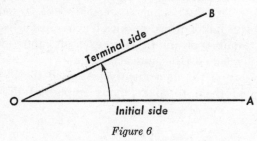

Figure 6

In reading an angle, as AOB, a letter on the initial side is read
first, then the letter at the vertex, and lastly a letter on the terminal

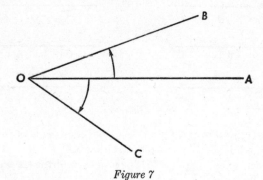

Figure 7

side.   The direction of rotation may be indicated by a curved
arrow.

Angles generated by rotating a line counter-clockwise are

generally regarded as positive, and those generated by rotating a line clockwise as negative.

In Figure 7, angle AOB is positive and angle AOC is negative. In general, $\angle AOB = -\angle BOA$, or $\angle AOB + \angle BOA = 0$.

Addition of Angles. To *add* the angle COD to the angle AOB, place angle AOB so that side OA falls on line XY. Then place the

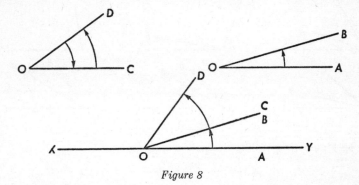

Figure 8

initial side OC of angle COD on the terminal side OB of the angle AOB and OD will fall as shown in Figure 8. The angle AOD is the *sum* of the angles AOB and COD or $\angle AOB + \angle COD = \angle AOD$.

To *add* the angle DOC to the angle AOB, place angle AOB so that side OA falls on line XY. Then place the initial arm OD of

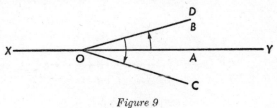

Figure 9

the angle DOC on the terminal arm OB of the angle AOB and OC will fall as shown in Figure 9. Thus $\angle AOB + \angle DOC = \angle AOC$. To *subtract* the angle COD from the angle AOB we may add the angle DOC to the angle AOB, that is, $\angle AOB - \angle COD = \angle AOB + \angle DOC$, which reduces to a problem of addition as above. The generalized addition as indicated here includes subtraction.

EXERCISES

1. In Figure 10 are shown the six possible arrangements of acute angles formed by the sides OA, OB, and OC, having a vertex O. Show in each case that $\angle AOC + \angle COB = \angle AOB$.

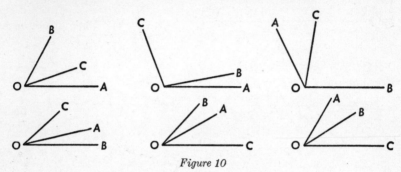

Figure 10

2. In Figure 10 show that in each arrangement

$$\angle AOC - \angle BOC = \angle AOB.$$

Consider only the acute angles in Figure 11 and express the result of each of the following with both the positive and the negative sign.

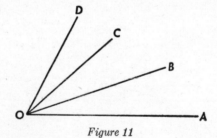

Figure 11

3. $\angle AOB + \angle BOC + \angle COD + \angle DOA = 0.$
4. $\angle AOC + \angle COB =$ 5. $\angle AOC + \angle COA =$
6. $\angle BOC + \angle COA =$ 7. $\angle DOA + \angle AOB =$
8. $\angle BOA + \angle AOC + \angle COD =$
9. $\angle DOC + \angle COB + \angle BOD + \angle DOC =$
10. $\angle DOC + \angle COB + \angle BOA =$
11. $\angle DOA + \angle AOB + \angle BOC =$
12. $\angle AOC - \angle BOC + \angle BOD =$

Internal Division of a Line Segment. A line segment AB is said to be divided *internally* by a point P which lies on AB between A and B.

In Figure 12, P divides AB internally into segments AP and PB which have the ratio AP/PB.

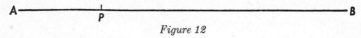

Figure 12

The following facts should be noted concerning this internal division and the resulting ratio:

1. $AP + PB = AB$.
2. Since P lies between A and B, AP and PB are measured in the same direction, and the ratio AP/PB is always positive.
3. If P coincides with A, $AP/PB = 0$.
4. If P is the midpoint of AB, $AP/PB = 1$.
5. If P is between A and the midpoint, $AP/PB < 1$.
6. If P is between the midpoint and B, $AP/PB > 1$.
7. As P moves from A to B the ratio increases from 0 to a larger and larger number.

EXERCISES

1. Recall three or more theorems of elementary geometry in which a line segment is divided internally into parts having a ratio of unity.
2. Prove that if in any triangle the bisector of an angle divides the opposite side into segments having a ratio of 1, the triangle is isosceles.

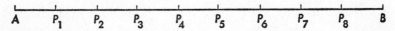

3. Find the ratio AP/PB for each position of P, the points being equally spaced.

External Division of a Line Segment. A line segment AB is said to be divided *externally* by a point P which lies on AB extended.

In Figure 13, P divides AB externally into segments AP and PB whose ratio is AP/PB.

Figure 13

Note the following facts concerning this external division and the resulting ratio:

1. $AP + PB = AB$.
2. Since AP and PB are measured in opposite directions, the ratio AP/PB is negative.
3. If B is between A and P, then AP/PB is greater in absolute value than 1; and as P moves away from B the ratio of division decreases in absolute value and approaches -1.
4. If A lies between B and P, then AP/PB is less in absolute value than 1; and as P moves away from A the ratio of division increases in absolute value and approaches -1.

THEOREM 1. *A line segment may be divided internally, or externally, in a given ratio in only one point.*

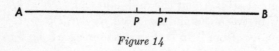

Figure 14

Suppose that both P and P' divide AB internally in the ratio h/k.

Then $\dfrac{AP}{PB} = \dfrac{AP'}{P'B}.$

Then $\dfrac{AP + PB}{PB} = \dfrac{AP' + P'B}{P'B}$ and $\dfrac{AB}{PB} = \dfrac{AB}{P'B}.$

Now show that P and P' coincide.
Prove the theorem for a point of external division.

EXERCISE

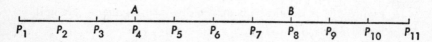

Find the ratio AP/PB for each position of P, for which a ratio exists, the points being equally spaced.

Positive and Negative Arcs. Arcs, like angles, are considered positive if traced counter-clockwise, and negative if traced clockwise. In Figure 15, $\widehat{AB}$ is positive and $\widehat{BA}$ is negative.

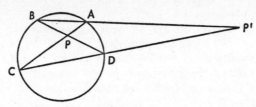

Figure 15

The arcs intercepted by the lines intersecting at P are both positive if the angles at P are read positively. If the angle at P' is read positively, one intercepted arc, BC, is positive, and the other, AD, is negative.

We may then state the following

THEOREM 2. *The angle formed by two lines that meet a circle is measured by one-half the sum of the intercepted arcs.*

Let the student prove this theorem. Be sure that the proof holds for all cases including two tangents, a tangent and a chord, a tangent and a secant, two secants, two chords intersecting within the circle, and two chords intersecting on the circle. Find the corresponding theorems in the appendix.

This theorem is another example of the simplicity and generality given to geometric statements resulting from the use of directed magnitudes.

EXERCISES

1. State the special case of Theorem 2 that would apply when: (a) the lines intersect on the circle, (b) the lines intersect at the center of the circle.
2. Find the angle formed by two tangents to a circle if the ratio of their intercepted arcs is $-\frac{1}{2}$.
3. In Figure 15 if $\widehat{DA} = 60°$ and $\widehat{BC} = 85°$, find (a) $\angle P'$; (b) $\angle BPC$; (c) $\angle BAC$; (d) $\angle P'DB$.
4. In Figure 15 if $\angle P' = 30°$ and $\widehat{DA} = 56°$, find $\angle APB$.

5. A point P divides the line segment XY internally. Where must P lie so that the ratio XP/PY is (a) unity? (b) zero? (c) a proper fraction? (d) an improper fraction? (e) What is the sign of XP/PY? (f) What change is made in XP/PY as P approaches closer and closer to Y?

6. A point P divides the line segment XY externally. What is the sign of XP/PY? Is the numerical value of XP/PY greater or less than unity if (a) Y is between X and P? (b) X is between Y and P? What change is made in the value of XP/PY when P moves off farther and farther (a) from X to the left? (b) from Y to the right?

7. AB is 12 in. long. Find AP/PB when AP has each of the following lengths: (a) 3 in.; (b) 8 in.; (c) 6 in.; (d) 11 in.; (e) 11.99 in.; (f) 12.01 in.; (g) 20 in.; (h) 1 mile; (i) -6 in.; (j) -40 in.; (k) -1 mile.

8. AB is 12 in. long. Find the lengths of AP and PB so that the ratio AP/PB has each of the following values: 1/3; 1; 3; 0.1; 100; -2; -60; -0.01.

9. Let O, A, B, be three points on a line arranged in any order, and let C be the midpoint of AB.

$$\text{Prove that } OC = \frac{OA + OB}{2}.$$

10. Let O, A, B, be any three points on a line and let C divide AB so that $p \cdot AC = q \cdot CB$.

$$\text{Prove that } OC = \frac{p \cdot OA + q \cdot OB}{p + q}.$$

11. A chord and a tangent intersect on a circle, making an angle of 65°. Find the arcs into which the circle is divided by the chord.

12. In Figure 15, page 9, as P' moves farther and farther to the right, angle P' approaches what value? The lines BP' and CP' approach what position? These questions suggest another proposition of elementary geometry which may be considered as a special case of Theorem 2. Can you state it?

CHAPTER 2

Points at Infinity

Definitions. If a variable becomes and remains larger than any constant that can be named in advance, the variable is said to *become infinite*.

Consider the quotient a/x, where a is a constant, not zero. If now x approaches zero as a limit, a/x is said to become infinite.

Division by zero has no meaning and is excluded from algebra.

If a point P moves off on a line so that its distance from a fixed point on a line becomes greater than any distance that can be named in advance, then P is said to move off to *infinity*.

The notion of points at infinity is frequently made use of in geometry. We now give some examples.

Example 1. If a line CD passing through a fixed point P be turned counter-clockwise, its point of intersection Q with a fixed line AB

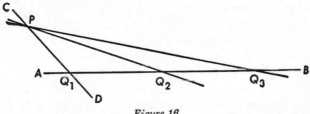

Figure 16

may be made to move to the right past any point R on AB, no matter how far out R may lie on AB. We say then that the point of intersection moves off to infinity along AB. See Figure 16.

Is there a position of CD such that it does not intersect AB? What exception, if any, is there to this statement: Two lines in the same plane always intersect?

Example 2. It is proved in elementary geometry that a circle may be passed through three points A, B, C, as in Figure 17. How is the center O of this circle found?

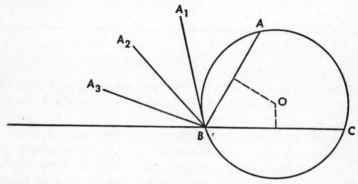

Figure 17

Suppose that the positions of the points B and C and the length of BA remain the same, and that the segment BA is rotated around B, taking the positions $BA_1, BA_2, BA_3, \cdots$. As A moves, will O, the center of the circle, move? Construct a figure to illustrate your answer.

Thus as BA is rotated counter clockwise to a position so that A lies almost on the line CB, how does the position of O change? What happens to the length of the radius of the circle? What is then the position of the arc ABC? As BA is rotated clockwise, how does O move? As BA approaches nearer and nearer BC, how does the position of O change? What is the locus of O as BA rotates? Can we have a circle passing through A, B, and C after BA rotates far enough so that A lies on the same line as B and C?

What exception, if any, is there to the statement: A circle may be made to pass through any three points?

Example 3. In Figure 18 AB is divided internally and externally in the same numerical ratio at C and D, that is. numerically

$$AC/CB = AD/DB.$$

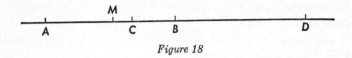

Figure 18

Suppose that $AB = 12$, and that $AC/CB = 2 : 1$. Then $AC = 8$, and $CB = 4$. Let us find AD.

Let $BD = x$. Then $AD = x + 12$, and $\dfrac{x + 12}{x} = \dfrac{2}{1}$.

Solving, $x = 12$, and $AD = 24$.

Find AC and AD when AC/CB approaches unity by taking on these values: 1.1; 1.01; 1.001.

As the ratio AC/CB approaches 1, what position does C approach? What becomes of D?

What will be the position of D when C approaches the midpoint M?

If a line is divided internally and externally in the ratio *unity*, what is the position of (a) the point of internal division? (b) the point of external division?

What exception, if any, is there to the statement: A line may be divided internally and externally in a given ratio?

The notion of infinite numbers was familiar to the ancient Greek mathematicians. So was that of infinite space. Anaximander of Miletus, about 600 B.C., is given credit for being the first to say that the world is infinite. The urge to solve the mathematical and logical implications of the infinite has been one of the most potent influences in the development of mathematics.

One modern mathematician calls mathematics the science of the infinite. It still offers unsolved riddles.

From the preceding examples it appears that

(a) Any two straight lines in the same plane intersect, *except* two parallel lines.

(b) A circle may be made to pass through any three points, *except* three collinear points.

(c) A line may be divided internally and externally in the same ratio, *except* the ratio unity.

The exceptions may be removed by adopting the concept of *points at infinity*.

We may state (a) without exception if we agree that two parallel lines meet in a point at infinity.

We may state (b) without exception if we agree that the center of the circle passing through three collinear points is a point at infinity.

We may state (c) without exception if we agree that the point of external division is a point at infinity when the ratio is unity.

The concept of points at infinity allows the statement, without exception, of many results, as we shall see throughout this book, that could not otherwise be made general. This leads to convenience and elegance in stating geometrical conclusions.

If in Figure 16 page 11, the line *CD* had been turned clockwise about *P* the point of intersection of *CD* and *AB* would have moved off to infinity toward the left. If we now say that this is a different point at infinity from the one determined by the point of intersection obtained by moving off to the right, we shall have the possibility of two parallel lines meeting in two points at infinity. Such a possibility may be avoided by assuming that a line has only one point at infinity. It is to be remembered that all points and lines in this discussion lie in one plane.

It follows from this assumption that *all the lines of a pencil of parallels go through the same point at infinity*.

Since there is one and only one point at infinity in a given direction it seems reasonable to regard *all the points at infinity as lying on a line which we shall call the line at infinity*.

Let us examine the concept of a circle with an infinite radius. Let the circle Figure 19 with center *O* be tangent to the line *AB* at *P*. If now the radius *OP* increases but the circle remains tangent to the line *AB* at *P*, as the center *O* goes off to infinity the lower part of the circle approaches nearer and nearer the line *AB*, while the upper part of the circle goes off to infinity. Hence we say that a circle with infinite radius consists of a straight line in the finite portion of the plane plus the line at infinity.

Any straight line that meets this circle will meet it in one finite point and one point at infinity.

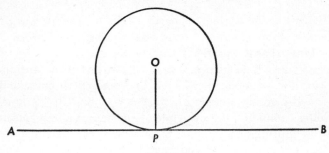

Figure 19

Historical Note. Johann Kepler (1571–1630) first introduced the notion of points at infinity into geometry, but Gerald Desargues (1593–1662) was the first to use the idea in his geometric theory. He assumed that parallel lines meet at infinity and that a cylinder is a cone with vertex at infinity.

In a work published in 1639 he introduced the notions of a point at infinity, the line at infinity, and a straight line as the limit of circle of infinite radius. Points and lines at infinity are called *ideal elements*.

EXERCISES

1. What does it mean to say that a variable becomes infinite?
2. What does it mean to say that a point moves off to infinity?
3. We have assumed that every line has how many points at infinity?
4. What is meant by the line at infinity in a plane?
5. State an exception to each of the following statements unless we use the concept of points at infinity:
   (a) Any two straight lines in the plane intersect.
   (b) A circle may be made to pass through any three points.
   (c) A line may be divided internally and externally in the same ratio.
6. State several examples from elementary geometry of a variable approaching a limit.

7. What is the limiting form of a circle as its radius becomes infinite?
8. What is the locus of all points at infinity in a given direction?
9. May three parallel lines be thought of as being concurrent?
10. Into what ratio does the bisector of an exterior angle at the vertex of an isosceles triangle divide the base?   Explain.

The Principle of Continuity.   The use of points at infinity as points on a curve is an example of the *principle of continuity*.   This principle says that if a property be true as a geometric figure varies and approaches a limiting position, it will also be true in the limiting position.   For example, consider a line passing through a fixed point O and meeting a circle in two points A and B.   If now the line rotates around O, the principle of continuity allows us to say that in its limiting position as a tangent it meets the circle in two coincident points, and if it continues to rotate in the same direction the two points of intersection become imaginary.   The student has met the same idea in solving a quadratic equation which is found always to have two solutions, real and unequal, equal, or imaginary.

The principle of continuity allows us to generalize many theorems and extend them to special cases.

CHAPTER 3 Similar Figures

Similar Polygons. Similar **polygons** are polygons whose corresponding angles are equal and whose corresponding sides are proportional.

THEOREM 3. *Two triangles are similar*
(a) *if they are mutually equiangular;*
(b) *or if an angle of one equals an angle of the other and the sides including the equal angles are proportional;*
(c) *or if their corresponding sides are proportional.*

COROLLARY. *Two triangles are similar if two angles of one equal two angles of the other.*

The proofs of these theorems are given in elementary geometry.

EXERCISES

1. Prove Theorem (a). **2.** Prove Theorem (b). **3.** Prove Theorem (c).
4. If a perpendicular is drawn from the vertex of the right angle of a right triangle to the hypotenuse, (a) the two triangles thus formed are similar to the given triangle and to each other; (b) the perpendicular is the mean proportional between the segments of the hypotenuse; and (c) each leg of the right triangle is the mean proportional between the hypotenuse and its adjacent segment. The *mean proportional* between two numbers is the square root of their product. See Figure 20.

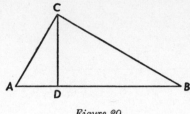

Figure 20

5. The perpendicular to the diameter from any point on a circle is the mean proportional between the segments of the diameter.
6. Construct a mean proportional between any two line segments.

PROBLEM 1. *To divide a line segment internally into parts having a given ratio.*

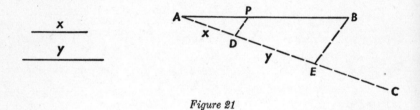

Figure 21

Let it be required to divide AB internally into parts having the ratio x/y.

Through A draw a line AC. On AC lay off $AD = x$, and $DE = y$. Join E and B and through D draw a line parallel to EB, thus determining the point P. Then, by Theorem 69, page 122, $AP/PB = x/y$, and P is the desired point of division.

PROBLEM 2. *To divide a line segment externally into parts having a given numerical ratio.*

Let it be required to divide AB externally into parts having the ratio x/y. See Figure 22.

Through A draw any line AC and on it lay off $AD = x$, and in the opposite direction lay off $DE = y$. Connect E and B and through D draw a line parallel to BE, cutting AB at P.

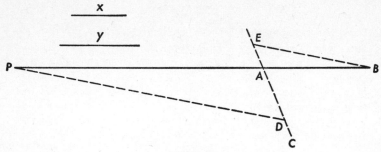

Figure 22

Then not regarding signs	Then $\dfrac{BA + AP}{AP} = \dfrac{EA + AD}{AD}$
$\dfrac{BA}{AP} = \dfrac{EA}{AD}.$	and $\dfrac{PB}{AP} = \dfrac{y}{x}$ or $\dfrac{AP}{PB} = \dfrac{x}{y}.$

THEOREM 4. *If through a fixed point a variable line is drawn to meet a circle, the product of the segments into which the point divides the variable chord cut from the line by the circle is constant.*

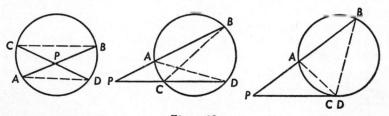

Figure 23

Let P be the fixed point.

Let AB and CD be any two positions of the variable chord.

Prove $\triangle PCB \sim \triangle PAD$.

Then $AP : CP = PD : PB$ and $AP \cdot PB = CP \cdot PD$.

Be sure that your argument holds for all three figures both as to magnitude and sign of the products.

Note that this theorem includes Theorems 79, 80, and 81, page 123. Let the student state these three theorems.

EXERCISES

1. Does Theorem 4 apply when the fixed point is on the circle? Does it apply when both intersecting lines are tangents?
2. Tangents drawn to two intersecting circles from any point on their common chord extended are equal.
3. If the common chord of two intersecting circles is extended, it bisects their common tangent.
4. Construct a circle passing through two given points and tangent to a given line; two constructions. (Use Problem 19, page 124.)

Definition. Points lying on the same circle are said to be *concyclic*.

THEOREM 5. *If AB and CD intersect at P and AP · PB = CP · PD, then A, B, C, D are concyclic.*

Pass a circle through *A, B, C* and prove that *D* cannot fall within or without this circle without violating Theorem 4.

EXERCISES

1. If through any point on the common chord of two intersecting circles two chords are drawn, one in each circle, their extremities are concyclic.
2. The vertices of any regular polygon are concyclic points.
3. The vertices of an isoseles trapezoid are concyclic points.
4. The vertices of a parallelogram are concyclic if, and only if, its diagonals are equal. What parallelograms are then inscriptible in a circle?
5. Medians are drawn from the equal angles *A* and *B* of a triangle, intersecting the opposite sides in *A'* and *B'* respectively. Prove that *A, B, A'* and *B'* are concyclic points.

Methods of Attack

1. *Four lines are usually proved to be proportional by showing them to be corresponding parts of similar triangles.*

2. *To prove that the product of two lines equals the product of two other lines, we usually show that the four lines form a proportion by being corresponding parts of similar triangles, and then use the theorem that the product of the means equals the product of the extremes.*

EXERCISES

1. A line parallel to the base of a triangle cuts off a triangle similar to the given triangle.
2. Corresponding altitudes of two similar triangles have the same ratio as any two corresponding sides.
3. How far from a circle whose radius is 6 must a point be selected so that the whole secant from that point through the center of the circle shall be twice the tangent from that point to the circle?
4. The corresponding medians of two similar triangles have the same ratio as any two corresponding sides.
5. If lines are drawn connecting the midpoints of the sides of a triangle, the figure contains five similar triangles.
6. The diagonals of a trapezoid divide each other into proportional segments.
7. If two fixed parallel tangents are cut by a variable tangent, the product of the segments of the latter formed by the parallel tangents and the point of contact is constant.
8. The common internal tangent of two circles divides their line of centers into parts proportional to the diameters of the circles.
9. AB and AC are the equal sides of an isosceles triangle, and BF and AO are the altitudes. Prove that $2AC \times FC = \overline{BC}^2$.
10. ABC is an inscribed triangle with CE the bisector of angle ACB, E being a point on the circle and D the point of intersection of CE and AB. Prove that $AD \cdot CB = EB \cdot CD$.
11. Prove that the product of any side of a triangle and the altitude to it is equal to the product of any other side and the altitude to it.
12. If two circles are tangent externally and a secant is drawn through the point of contact, the chords formed are proportional to the diameters of the circles.
13. If two circles are tangent externally, the common external tangent is the mean proportional between the diameters.
14. In a triangle the product of any two sides is equal to the product of the altitude to the third side and the diameter of the circumscribed circle.
15. If a chord of a circle is bisected by a second chord, either part of the first chord is a mean proportional between the segments of the other.
16. The area of a triangle is 64 square inches. Lines parallel to the base divide one side into three equal segments. Find the area of each of the three parts into which the triangle is divided.

PROBLEMS

1. Construct a triangle similar to a given triangle with a pair of corresponding sides having a ratio of 2/3.

2. Construct a triangle similar to a given triangle having an area of one-half the given triangle.

3. Construct a triangle similar to a given triangle and having a given perimeter.

4. Inscribe in a given circle a triangle similar to a given triangle.

5. Draw a line parallel to one side of a given triangle, cutting off another triangle having a given perimeter.

6. Divide a line segment AB into parts having a ratio of: 1/2; 2/3; −1/2; −3; −3/2; 3/4; 5/7.

7. The ratio, $-\dfrac{1}{3}$, may be expressed either as $\dfrac{-1}{+3}$ or $\dfrac{+1}{-3}$.

Divide the segment AB into the ratio of (a) $\dfrac{-1}{+3}$ and (b) $\dfrac{+1}{-3}$, and

prove that the points of division are identical.

8. Construct a rectangle having a given base and equivalent to a given square.

9. Given a line segment a, construct line segments having values of

(a) $\sqrt{3}\,a$, (b) $\sqrt{2}\,a$, (c) $\dfrac{1}{\sqrt{3}}\,a$.

Similar and Homothetic Figures. If two points P and Q move in a plane so that the line PQ always passes through a fixed point

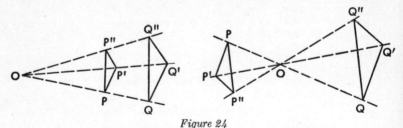

Figure 24

O which divides the segment PQ in a constant ratio k, $OP/OQ = k$, then the paths of P and Q are said to be *similar and similarly placed figures*, or *homothetic figures*.

O is called the *center of similitude* and k the *ratio of similitude* of the two figures.

P and Q are said to be *corresponding points* in the two figures.

The two figures are said to be *directly* or *inversely homothetic* according as O divides PQ externally or internally; and O is called the *external* or *internal center of similitude* respectively.

The ratio of similitude is positive if the figures are directly homothetic, and negative if inversely homothetic.

The two figures are said to be in *perspective* and O is called the *center of perspective*.

THEOREM 6. *The segment joining any two points in one of two homothetic figures is parallel to the segment joining the corresponding points in the other, and the ratio of the segments equals the ratio of similitude.*

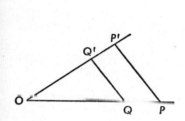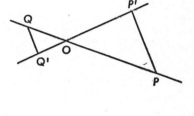

Figure 25

Let P and P' be any two points in one of two homothetic figures and Q and Q' their corresponding points in the other, and O the center of similitude of the two figures.

Then since $OP/OQ = OP'/OQ' = k$, and $\angle POP' = \angle QOQ'$,

$$\triangle OPP' \sim \triangle OQQ', \quad \text{(Theorem 3b, page 17)}.$$

$$\therefore \ \angle OP'P = \angle OQ'Q \quad \text{and} \quad PP' \parallel QQ',$$

and $PP'/QQ' = k$.

COROLLARY. *The homothetic figure of a straight line is a straight line parallel to the given line.*

EXERCISES

Exercises 3–7 on page 27.

THEOREM 7. *Any two circles are both directly and inversely homo-*
thetic and their centers of similitude are the points which divide the
line of centers externally and internally into segments having the
ratio of the radii.

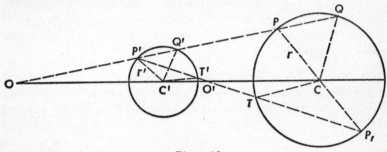

Figure 26

Given circles with centers C and C' and radii r and r'. Let
CP and $C'P'$ be parallel radii drawn in the same direction and $CP_{\prime}$
and $C'P'$ parallel radii drawn in opposite directions. Draw $PP_{\prime}$
intersecting circle C in Q and circle C' in Q' and the line of centers
in O; and $P_{\prime}P'$ intersecting circle C in T and circle C' in T' and
the line of centers in O', respectively.

$$\triangle OCP \sim \triangle OC'P'$$

$$\therefore OP : OP' = OC : OC' = r : r'.$$

Draw CQ and $C'Q'$ and prove them parallel

$$(\angle P'Q'C' = \angle C'P'Q' \quad \text{and} \quad \angle PQC = \angle CPQ).$$

Then $OQ : OQ' = OC : OC' = r : r'$, and Q and Q' are corresponding points.

$$\therefore O \text{ is the external center of similitude.}$$

Similarly, $O'P_{\prime} : O'P' = O'C : O'C' = r : r'.$

and $\qquad O'T : O'T' = O'C : O'C' = r : r'.$ (Prove it.)

$$\therefore O' \text{ is the internal center of similitude.}$$

COROLLARY.   *If two circles have common external tangents, these tangents pass through the external center of similitude and if they have common internal tangents, these tangents pass through their internal center of similitude.*

THEOREM 8.   *Two similar polygons with their corresponding sides parallel are homothetic.*

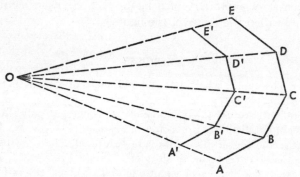

Figure 27

Let $ABCDE \cdots$ and $A'B'C'D'E' \cdots$ be similar polygons with their corresponding sides parallel.

Let AA' and BB' intersect in O.   Then,

$$OA : OA' = OB : OB' = AB : A'B'.$$

If now BB' and CC' intersect in some point O',

$$O'B : O'B' = O'C : O'C' = BC : B'C' = OB : OB'.$$

$\therefore$ O' coincides with O on BO by Theorem 1, page 8.

$\therefore$ Lines through corresponding vertices are concurrent.

Furthermore, any line through O cutting $ABCDE \cdots$ in any point X will cut $A'B'C'D'E' \cdots$ in a point X' so that $OX : OX' = AB : A'B'$.   The figures are therefore homothetic.

The above theorem may be generalized to include any two similar figures, since it is true even though the figures consist of curves as well as straight lines.

Symmetry with Respect to a Point. If the ratio of similitude of two figures is -1, the figures are said to be *symmetric* with respect to the center of similitude. The center of similitude is then called the *center of symmetry* of the two figures.

This definition is evidently equivalent to saying that two figures are symmetric with respect to a point if the point bisects the lines joining corresponding points.

The center of symmetry of a figure, as a circle or a square, is commonly called the *center* of the figure.

EXERCISES

1. Prove Theorem 8 when AA' and BB' meet in a point between A and A'.
2. Where is the center of similitude of two congruent polygons whose sides are parallel? Is it a center of symmetry?
3. What is the center of similitude of two parallel lines? Have they more than one center of similitude?
4. Construct the centers of similitude of two given (a) intersecting circles; (b) non-intersecting circles; (c) externally tangent circles; (d) internally tangent circles; (e) one circle entirely within the other.
5. Do two concentric circles have centers of similitude? If so, where are they?
6. The line joining the outer extremeties of parallel radii of two circles passes through their external center of similitude if they extend in the same direction from the centers; and through their internal center of similitude if they extend in opposite directions.
7. If a third circle is tangent externally to two given circles, the line joining the points of contact passes through a center of similitude of the two given circles.
8. The line from O, the external center of similitude, to a point of intersection of two circles, is a mean proportional between the tangents to the circles from O.
9. The radii of two circles are r_1 and r_2 and the distance between their centers is d. Find the distance between their centers of similitude. What is this distance when $r_1 = r_2$?
10. Any secant drawn through the direct center of similitude O of two circles cuts the circles in points whose distances from O taken in order form a proportion.

The Pantograph. The *pantograph*, invented in 1603 by Christopher Scheiner, is an instrument used for drawing a figure homothetic to a given figure. It is used for enlarging and reducing maps and diagrams. The pantograph consists of four equal bars pivoted at A, B, P, and C so that $BPCA$ is a parallelogram and

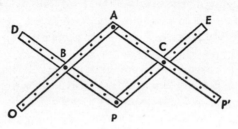

Figure 28

$OB = BP$ and $PC = CP'$. Pencils are fastened at P and P'. The point O is fixed and OA rotates about it. As P traces a given figure, P' will trace a homothetic one, or as P' traces a figure, P will trace its homothetic figure.

EXERCISES

1. In Figure 28, prove that O, P, and P' are collinear points.
2. Prove that $\dfrac{OP}{OP'} = \dfrac{OB}{OA}$.
3. Join a fixed point O to the vertices of a square $ABCD$. Bisect OA, OB, OC, OD at A', B', C', D' respectively. What kind of polygon is $A'B'C'D'$? Prove it. What is the ratio of AB to $A'B'$?
4. Draw a circle of radius 3 in. Take a point O, 8 in. from its center. Join O to a variable point P on the circle, and let Q bisect OP. Plot the locus of Q as P traces out the circle.
5. Plot the locus of Q in Exercise 4 if Q divides OP in the ratio $-$ 2:1. What is the locus of Q if $OP : OQ = -1$?
6. Construct a triangle homothetic to a given triangle, having a ratio of similitude of: (a) 2, (b) $-1/2$, (c) 1. Compare the areas of each pair of homothetic figures.
7. Construct a figure homothetic to a given figure and having a ratio of similitude of: (a) 2; (b) -2; (c) 1.

The Beginnings of Geometry.   Geometry was first studied because it was useful.   Such studies date back to 3000 B.C.   In surveying land, in building temples and monuments, in finding areas and volumes, in measuring heights and distances, and in attempting to solve the mysteries of astronomy in which ancient scholars were intensely interested, there arose the need for geometrical facts. The word *geometry* is derived from two Greek words meaning " earth " and " to measure " and early geometry was closely allied to surveying.

Geometrical conclusions were first arrived at intuitively and tested experimentally.   Some of these conclusions were inaccurate. The Hebrews used 3 for the value of π and the Babylonians found the value of the frustum of a cone by multiplying the sum of the bases by one-half the altitude.   Such approximations were also used by the Egyptians, Chinese, and Hindus.

The ancient Greeks were the first to attempt a scientific approach to geometry.   Greek interest in demonstrative geometry began with Thales of Miletus, who lived about 600 B.C., and was one of the Seven Wise Men of Greece.   He is credited with proving a half-dozen of the simpler propositions of geometry.   This accomplishment may seem scarcely sufficient to give Thales the title of Father of Geometry.   But the honor is justified if he is credited with the impetus that made geometry the model for logical thought.

Definition. If a variable point moves subject to a given condition, the path it describes is called its *locus*.

In order to prove that a figure is a locus it is necessary and sufficient to prove two things: (1) That every point on the figure satisfies the given condition. (2) That every point which satisfies the given condition lies on the figure. This involves proof of a theorem and its converse. This method is illustrated below.

THEOREM 9. *The locus of a point equally distant from two given points is the perpendicular bisector of the line joining them.*

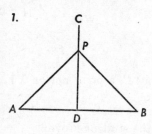 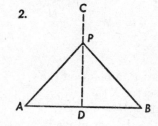

Figure 29

Given: CD is the ⊥ bisector of AB.
Prove: $PA = PB$. (Prove it)

Given: $PA = PB$, and D the midpoint of AB.
Prove: $CD \perp AB$. (Prove it)

The preceding proof of Theorem 9 involves the proving of the two following converse theorems.

1. *Every point in the perpendicular bisector of a line is equally distant from the ends of the line.*

2. *Every point equally distant from the ends of a line lies in the perpendicular bisector of the line.*

Part 1 proves that every point on the perpendicular bisector satisfies the given condition and part 2 proves that there can be no part of the locus outside of this perpendicular bisector.

A figure may also be proved to be a locus by showing that: (1) Every point on the figure satisfies the given condition.   (2) Any point not on the figure does not satisfy the given condition.   This method involves the proof of a theorem and its opposite as illustrated in the proof of Theorem 10.

THEOREM 10.   *The locus of a point equally distant from two intersecting lines consists of the bisectors of their included angles.*

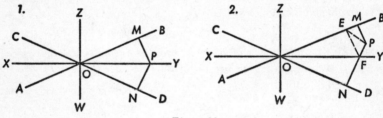

Figure 30

Given: P, a point on the bisector XY.	Given: P, a point not on XY.
Prove: $PM = PN$.	Prove: $PN \neq PM$.
Let the student prove it.	Let the student prove it.

Let the student prove the following locus theorems.

THEOREM 11.   *The locus of a point equally distant from two parallel lines is a line parallel to the given lines and midway between them.*

THEOREM 12. *The locus of a point at a given distance from a given line is two lines parallel to the given line and at the given distance from it.*

THEOREM 13. *The locus of a point at a given distance from a given point is a circle with the given point as the center and the given distance as a radius.*

EXERCISES

1. What is the locus of a point x distance from a circle of radius r, when x is less than r; when x equals r; when x is greater than r?
2. What is the locus of the center of a circle having a constant radius, (a) if the circle touches a given line; (b) if the circle touches a given circle; (c) if the circle passes through a given point?
3. What is the locus of the vertex of a triangle on a given base and having a given area?
4. What is the locus of the centers of all circles passing through two fixed points?
5. What is the locus of the center of a circle as it (1) rolls around a square, (2) as it rolls within a square?
6. Prove Theorem 9 by proving a theorem and its opposite.
7. Prove Theorem 10 by proving a theorem and its converse.
8. What is the locus of a point equally distant from a given point and a given straight line?

Historical Note. *Euclidian Geometry.* The concepts and methods of elementary geometry go back to Euclid. He lived about 300 B.C. in Alexandria. He collected, systematized, and added to the mass of material treating of circles, rectilinear figures, and ratios that had accumulated since the time of Thales and combined it into his *Elements.* The most remarkable feature of his work lies in furnishing logical proofs in logical order. It is a landmark in scientific progress. It is the greatest of all textbooks in elementary mathematics, and more than a thousand editions are said to have appeared since 1482. The methods and subject matter of the *Elements* still dominate the teaching of elementary geometry. Many of the theorems of the first five chapters of this book go back to Euclid. His method of proof, the synthetic method, is used throughout.

Intersection of Two Loci. A locus satisfying two conditions is found by discovering the intersection or intersections of the loci satisfying each condition.

Example: Find all points that are at a given distance r from a given point A, and also equally distant from the points B and C.

The locus of a point r distance from A is a circle with A as a center and r as a radius. The locus of a point equally distant from C and D is the perpendicular bisector of the line segment joining them. Therefore, the required points will be the intersection of the circle and the perpendicular bisector. There may be two, one, or no points fulfilling both requirements.

EXERCISES

In each of the following, state what the locus is and discuss the number of solutions, special cases, and tell when a solution is impossible.

1. Find all points that are equally distant from the sides of a given angle and also equally distant from two given points.
2. Find all points on a given line that are at a given distance from a given point.
3. Find all points at a given distance from a given circle and also at a given distance from a given line which intersects the circle.
4. Find all points that are equally distant from points A and B and also equally distant from points C and D.
5. Find all points that are equally distant from two given parallel lines and also at a given distance from a given line.
6. Find all points equally distant from two given parallel lines and also equally distant from two given intersecting lines.
7. Find all points at a given distance from a given line and also at a given distance from a given point.
8. Find the centers of all circles which pass through a given point and also touch a given line.

PROBLEM 3. *On a given line segment, to construct a segment of a circle which shall contain a given angle.*

Let AB be the given line and $\angle C$ the given angle. Figure 31.

Required to construct on AB a segment of a circle which shall contain an angle equal to $\angle C$.

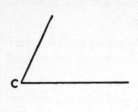

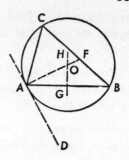

Figure 31

Draw *AD* making ∠*DAB* = ∠*C*. Construct *AF* ⊥ *AD*. Construct *GH* the ⊥ bisector of *AB*. With *O* as a center and *OA* as a radius construct a circle which will pass through *B*. Then *BCA* is the required segment and ∠*ACB* = the given ∠*C*.

For: *AD* is a tangent to circle *O* and ∠*DAB* = any angle as ∠*ACB* inscribed in the segment *BCA*. (Theorems 60, 62, page 122.)

THEOREM 14. *The locus of a point on one side of a given line segment at which this segment subtends a given angle is an arc of a circle passing through the ends of the given segment.*

Let *AB* (Figure 31) be the given line and *C* be the given angle. Then (1) any point *C* on the arc *BCA* satisfies the given condition and (2) any point *C* without or within the circle does not satisfy the given condition by Theorem 2, page 9.

COROLLARY. *The locus of a point at which a given line segment subtends a right angle is a circle having the given line segment for its diameter.*

Definition. A *cyclic quadrilateral* is one that can be inscribed in a circle.

THEOREM 15. *In a cyclic quadrilateral the sum of two opposite angles equals the sum of the other two opposite angles.* Let the student prove this theorem.

COROLLARY. *Two opposite angles of a cyclic quadrilateral are supplementary.*

43260

THEOREM 16. *If the sum of two opposite angles of a quadrilateral equals the sum of the other two opposite angles, the quadrilateral is cyclic.*

Prove by passing a circle through three vertices of the quadrilateral and by proving that the fourth vertex cannot fall without or within this circle.

COROLLARY. *If two opposite angles of a quadrilateral are supplementary, the quadrilateral is cyclic.*

Exercises 10–15, page 39.

THEOREM 17. (THE CIRCLE OF APOLLONIUS.) *The locus of a point, the ratio of whose distances from two fixed points is constant, is a circle.*

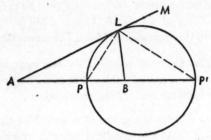

Figure 32

Let A and B be the two given points and let L be any point on the locus.

Then $\dfrac{LA}{LB} = k$, the given ratio.

Bisect the $\angle$s ALB and BLM, locating the points P and P' on the line AB.

P and P' are on the required locus.   (Theorems 102, 103, page 125.)

Proof: $\angle PLP' = \tfrac{1}{2}(\angle ALB + \angle BLM)$ = a right $\angle$.

$\therefore$ The locus of L is a circle with PP' as diameter. (By Theorem 14, Cor., page 33.)

THEOREM 18. (THEOREM OF APOLLONIUS.) *The locus of a point, the sum of the squares of whose distances from two fixed points is constant, is a circle whose center is the midpoint of the segment joining the two points*

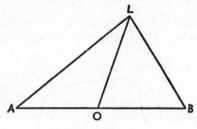

Figure 33

Given: $\overline{LA}^2 + \overline{LB}^2 = k$ (a constant).
Prove: The locus of L to be a circle with O the midpoint of AB its center.

$$\overline{LA}^2 + \overline{LB}^2 = 2\overline{AO}^2 + 2\overline{OL}^2. \quad \text{(Theorem 107, page 127.)}$$

$$\therefore \overline{OL}^2 = \frac{(\overline{LA}^2 + \overline{LB}^2) - 2\overline{AO}^2}{2}.$$

$\overline{LA}^2 + \overline{LB}^2 = $ the given constant k, and $2\overline{AO}^2$ is also a constant. (Why?)

$\therefore \overline{OL}^2$ is the difference between two known constants and is a constant.

$\therefore OL$ is a constant and L is at a fixed distance from O.

$\therefore$ The locus of L is a circle with O as its center. (Theorem 13, page 31.)

EXERCISES

1. What does the locus become in Theorem 17 if the given ratio is unity?
2. Construct a triangle having given its base, the ratio of its other two sides, and its altitude.
3. Construct a triangle having given the base, the angle opposite the base, and the ratio of the other two sides.

4. Discuss the change in size and position of the circle of Apollonius (Theorem 17) as the ratio k increases from 0 to 1; and then increases without limit.

5. Find the locus of a point the ratio of whose distances from two fixed points is 1 : 3.

THEOREM 19. (**PTOLEMY'S THEOREM.**) *In a cyclic quadrilateral the sum of the products of the opposite sides equals the product of the diagonals.*

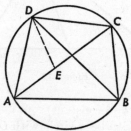

Figure 34

Prove: $AD \cdot BC + AB \cdot DC = AC \cdot BD$.
Draw DE making $\angle ADE = \angle BDC$.

$\triangle AED \sim \triangle BCD$, for $\angle ADE = \angle BDC$ and $\angle EAD = \angle CBD$.

$$\therefore \frac{AD}{AE} = \frac{BD}{BC}, \quad \text{and} \quad AD \cdot BC = AE \cdot BD.$$

Also $\triangle DAB \sim \triangle DEC$, for $\angle DBA = \angle DCE$, and $\angle ADB = \angle EDC$.

$$\therefore \frac{AB}{BD} = \frac{EC}{CD}, \quad \text{and} \quad AB \cdot CD = EC \cdot BD$$

$$\therefore AD \cdot BC + AB \cdot CD = AE \cdot BD + EC \cdot BD$$
$$= (AE + EC)BD = AC \cdot BD.$$

Historical Note. Ptolemy (*c.* 87–165 A.D.). A famous Greek astronomer and one of the earliest writers on astronomy. The above theorem is found in his great work on astronomy, the *Almagest*, which was an authority in its field for hundreds of years.

THEOREM 20. (CONVERSE OF PTOLEMY'S THEOREM.) *If in a quadrilateral the sum of the products of the opposite sides equals the product of the diagonals, the quadrilateral is cyclic.*

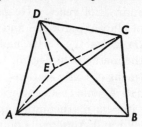

Figure 35

Given: The quadrilateral $ABCD$ with $AD \cdot BC + AB \cdot CD = AC \cdot BD$.

Prove: $ABCD$ a cyclic quadrilateral.

Proof: Construct $\triangle AED$ with $\angle ADE = \angle BDC$ and $\angle EAD = \angle CBD$.
Then $\triangle AED \sim \triangle BCD$.

$$\frac{AD}{AE} = \frac{DD}{BC} \quad \text{and} \quad AD \cdot BC = AE \cdot BD.$$

Also $\quad \dfrac{DE}{AD} = \dfrac{CD}{BD} \quad \text{and} \quad \angle EDC = \angle ADB.$

$\therefore \triangle ECD \sim \triangle ABD.$ (Theorem 3b, page 17.)

$\therefore \dfrac{CD}{EC} = \dfrac{BD}{AB} \quad \text{and} \quad AB \cdot CD = EC \cdot BD.$

$\therefore AD \cdot BC + AB \cdot CD = AE \cdot BD + EC \cdot BD$

or $\quad AD \cdot BC + AB \cdot CD = (AE + EC)BD.$

but $\quad AD \cdot BC + AB \cdot CD = AC \cdot BD$ (hypothesis).

$\therefore AE + EC = AC \quad$ and AEC is a straight line

and $\quad \angle CAD = \angle EAD = \angle CBD \quad$ (by construction).

$\therefore ABCD$ is cyclic.   (Theorem 14, page 33.)

Apollonius of Perga. A mathematician who studied and taught
in Alexandria about 225 B.C.; he was known as the Great Geometer
because of his work on the conic sections which was the authority
on that subject for hundreds of years. He gave the conic sections
their present names of ellipse, parabola, and hyperbola. He also
wrote other works on geometry. His methods of proof were
synthetic, similar to the methods of Euclid. We now use analytic
geometry in the treatment of conic sections. The great contribu-
tion of Greek mathematics came to an end with Apollonius. After
his death no great writer on mathematics appeared for two hun-
dred years. But Euclid and Apollonius dominated geometry for
twenty centuries.

EXERCISES

  1. Prove that the bisectors of the vertex angles of all the triangles
     that may be constructed on one side of a given base and having a
     given vertex angle are concurrent (meet in a point).
  *2. Find analytically the locus of a point (x,y) the sum of the squares
     of whose distances from the points $(4,4)$ and $(2,0)$ is 12. Does this
     equation represent a circle? Find its center and radius.
  *3. Find analytically the locus of a point (x,y) the ratio of whose
     distances from (a,b) and (c,d) is a constant k. Does this equation
     represent a circle?
  4. Find the locus of the midpoint of a variable chord passing through
     a fixed point within a circle. Prove. What is the locus when the
     fixed point is on the circle? Without the circle?
  5. Construct a triangle given the base, the median to the base and the
     vertex angle.
  6. Construct a triangle given the base, the vertex angle, and the foot
     of the altitude.
  7. Construct a right triangle given its hypotenuse and the altitude to
     the hypotenuse.
  8. Construct a triangle given two sides and an angle opposite one of
     them.
  9. Find a point within a triangle so that the lines joining it with the
     vertices form equal angles with each other. When is the solution
     impossible?

  * Exercises 2 and 3 may be omitted by those students who have not studied
analytical geometry.

10. Prove that in any triangle a vertex, the feet of the altitudes from the other two vertices, and the intersection of the altitudes, are concyclic points.

11. The circle having one of the equal sides of an isosceles triangle as a diameter passes through the midpoint of the base.

12. An exterior angle of a cyclic quadrilateral is equal to its opposite interior angle.

13. The bisector of an angle of an inscribed quadrilateral meets the bisector of the opposite exterior angle on the circumscribed circle.

14. The bisectors of the interior angles or of the exterior angles of any quadrilateral form a cyclic quadrilateral.

15. Construct a right triangle, given the hypotenuse and the sum of the other two sides.

16. Given a triangle ABC, find a point P such that $PA : PB : PC = 1 : 2 : 3$.

17. Construct the common internal tangents and the common external tangents of two circles.

18. A line OAB is drawn through the center of similitude O of two circles and cuts then at corresponding points A and B. Prove that the tangents at A and B are parallel.

CHAPTER 5   Properties of the Triangle

Notation. This notation will be used in the triangle ABC.

A, B, C, the vertices.

a, b, c, the length of the sides opposite the vertices A, B, C, respectively.

h_a, h_b, h_c, the altitudes to sides a, b, c, respectively.

m_a, m_b, m_c, the medians to sides a, b, c, respectively.

D, E, F, the feet of the altitudes from A, B, and C, respectively.

A', B', C', the midpoints of the sides opposite A, B, and C, respectively.

r, radius of the inscribed circle.

r', radius of the circumscribed circle.

S, circumcenter.

I, incenter, and I', I'', I''' the escribed centers on the bisectors of the internal angles A, B, and C, respectively.

H, orthocenter.

G, centroid.

P, Q, R, midpoints of HA, HB, and HC.

Definitions. Lines passing through the same point are said to be *concurrent*. Points lying on the same line are said to be *collinear*.

THEOREM 21. *The bisectors of the angles of a triangle are concurrent in a point equidistant from the sides of the triangle.*

Proof: AT and BW will intersect at some point I, Figure 36, (Theorem 18, page 120.) Draw ⊥s from I to the sides of the triangle. Then prove that $IK = IM$ and therefore CJ must pass through I by Theorem 10, page 30.

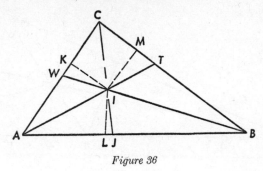

Figure 36

The point of intersection of the bisectors of the angles of a triangle is called the *incenter* of the triangle. It is the center of the inscribed circle.

EXERCISES

1. Any circle whose center is the incenter of a triangle, and which intersects the sides of the triangle, cuts off equal chords from the sides of the triangle, or from the sides extended.
2. An angle formed by the bisectors of any two angles of a triangle is obtuse.
3. The radius of an incircle of a right triangle is equal to half the difference of the sum of the two legs and the hypotenuse.
4. The base and vertex angle of a triangle being given, find the locus of the incenter of the triangle. Prove.
5. If CF is the altitude and CY the bisector of $\angle C$, of triangle ABC the angle $FCY = \frac{1}{2}(\angle A - \angle B)$.
6. An angle formed by the bisectors of two angles of a triangle is equal to a right angle plus half the third angle of the triangle.
7. An angle formed by the bisectors of two exterior angles of a triangle is equal to a right angle less half the third angle of the triangle.
8. The bisector of one angle of a triangle forms with the bisector of an exterior angle at a second vertex, an angle equal to half the third angle of the triangle.
9. If the bisectors of the angles of a quadrilateral are not concurrent, they form a cyclic quadrilateral.

THEOREM 22.   *Each angle bisector of a triangle if extended is concurrent with the bisectors of the exterior angles at the other two vertices.*

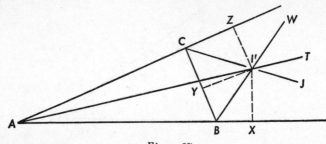

Figure 37

Proof: Prove that AT and BW cannot be parallel by Theorem 18, page 120, and therefore must meet at some point as I'.   Draw ⊥s from I' to the sides of the triangle.   Then prove that $I'Z = I'Y$ and therefore CJ must pass through I'.

The three points as I' are called the *excenters* of the triangle. They are the centers of the three *escribed circles* of the triangle.

COROLLARY 1.   *The incenter and the excenter of a triangle lying on the bisector of a given angle are the extremeties of the diameter of a circle passing through the other two vertices of the triangle.* Use Theorem 14, Cor., page 33.

COROLLARY. 2.   *The excenters I' and I'' which are located on the bisectors of angles A and B respectively are the extremeties of the diameter of a circle passing through A and B.*

EXERCISE

If from a fixed point A two tangents AB and AC are drawn to the circle O and at a variable point D on the arc BC a third tangent is drawn intersecting AB at E and AC at F, then O is an escribed circle of the triangle AEF whose perimeter is constant.

THEOREM 23. *If the bisectors of two angles of a triangle are equal, the triangle is isosceles.*

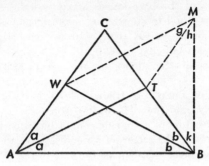

Figure 38

Proof: Use the indirect method of proof.

If the $\triangle$ is not isosceles, then $\angle A \neq \angle B$. Suppose either angle greater than the other.

Suppose $\angle A > \angle B$, then $\angle a > \angle b$, and $BT > AW$. (Theorem 42, page 121.)

Draw $WM \parallel AT$ and $TM \parallel AW$; draw BM.

$$ATMW \text{ is a } \square \quad \text{and} \quad WM = AT = BW.$$

Therefore $\triangle WBM$ is isosceles and

$$\angle g + \angle h = \angle b + \angle k.$$

But since $\angle g = \angle a > \angle b$, then $\angle h < \angle k$ and $BT < MT$ or AW, and $\angle A < \angle B$ which contradicts the supposition.

Therefore $\angle A = \angle B$ and the $\triangle$ is isosceles.

EXERCISES

1. Construct a triangle given two angles and the angle bisector of the third angle.
2. Through a given point within a given angle to draw a line which will form with the given angle a triangle having a given perimeter. Can you prove when the given point is without the angle?
3. The bisectors of the interior and exterior angles at two vertices of a triangle form a cyclic quadrilateral.

4. The bisectors of two exterior angles of a triangle form an angle which equals half the third exterior angle.
5. The bisectors of the base angles of an isosceles triangle form an angle which is equal to an exterior angle at the base.
6. The bisector of the vertex angle of an isosceles triangle bisects the base and is perpendicular to it.
7. The bisectors of the angles of any circumscribed polygon are concurrent.
8. The bisector of angle C of triangle ABC meets AB at J. Prove that $BC > BJ$, and that $AC > AJ$.
9. Two angle bisectors of a triangle cannot bisect each other.
10. If the bisectors of the angles of a quadrilateral are concurrent, the sum of two opposite sides equals the sum of the other two opposite sides. (Inscribe a circle.)

THEOREM 24. *The perpendicular bisectors of the sides of a triangle are concurrent in a point equidistant from the vertices of the triangle.*

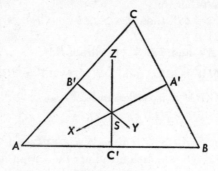

Figure 39

Prove that $A'X$, $B'Y$, and $C'Z$ are concurrent.

$B'Y$ and $A'X$ will meet at some point S.   (Theorem 17, page 120.)

Then $SB = SC$ and $SA = SC$. Therefore $SA = SB$ and S is on the perpendicular bisector of AB.

Definition. The point of intersection of the perpendicular bisectors of the sides of a triangle is called the *circumcenter* of the triangle. It is the center of the circumscribed circle.

THEOREM 25. *The altitudes of a triangle are concurrent.*

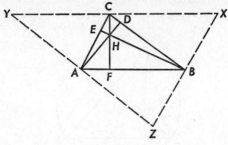

Figure 40

Prove that AD, BE, and CF are concurrent.

Proof: Draw YZ and ZX and XY through A, B, C, respectively and parallel to BC, CA, and AB.

Prove by using parallelograms that AD, BE, and CF are the perpendicular bisectors of the sides of the triangle XYZ and therefore concurrent.

Definitions. The point of intersection of the altitudes of a triangle is called the *orthocenter* of the triangle. The triangle formed by joining the feet of the altitudes of a triangle is called the *pedal* or *orthic triangle* of the given triangle.

EXERCISES

1. If H is the orthocenter of triangle ABC, then C is the orthocenter of triangle ABH, B is the orthocenter of triangle AHC, and A is the orthocenter of triangle BCH. Prove.
2. In what kind of triangle is the orthocenter within the triangle? on a vertex? without the triangle? Prove your answers.
3. Can the circumcenter and orthocenter of a triangle coincide?
4. In Figure 40 if C approaches nearer and nearer F along CF and AB remains fixed, what is the locus of H?
5. Given the base and the vertex angle of a triangle. Prove that the locus of the orthocenter consists of arcs of circles equal to the circumcircle of the triangle.

THEOREM 26. *If an altitude of a triangle is produced to the circumference of the circumscribed circle, the segment between the orthocenter
and the circumscribed circle is bisected by a side of the triangle.*

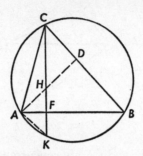

Figure 41

Prove that $HF = FK.$

Proof: $\angle FAH = \angle HCD.$ (Theorem 23, page 120.)

But $\angle HCD = \angle KAB,$

   $\therefore \ \angle KAF = \angle FAH,$

   $\therefore \ \triangle FAH \cong \triangle FAK,$ and $HF = FK.$

THEOREM 27. *Each altitude of a triangle bisects a corresponding
angle of the orthic triangle.*

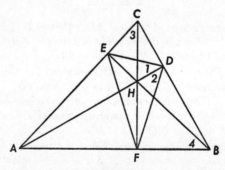

Figure 42

Prove that $\angle 1 = \angle 2$.

$EHDC$ is inscriptible.   (Theorem 16, page 34.)

$$\therefore \angle 1 = \angle 3.$$

$HFBD$ is inscriptible. $\therefore \angle 2 = \angle 4$.

$\angle 3 = \angle 4$.   (Theorem 23, page 120.) $\therefore \angle 1 = \angle 2$.

EXERCISES

1. An altitude from one of the equal angles of an isosceles triangle forms with the base an angle equal to half the vertex angle.
2. If from any point O within the triangle ABC the perpendiculars OX, OY, and OZ are drawn to the sides AB, BC, and CA respectively, then

$$\overline{AX}^2 + \overline{BY}^2 + \overline{CZ}^2 = \overline{BX}^2 + \overline{YC}^2 + \overline{ZA}^2.$$

3. If from the extremeties of a diameter perpendiculars are drawn to any chord (produced if necessary), the feet of these perpendiculars are equidistant from the center of the circle.
4. Prove that the orthocenter of any triangle is the incenter, or the excenter of its pedal triangle.
5. Prove that in any acute triangle the three sides are the bisectors of the exterior angles of the pedal triangle.
6. The three circles which pass through two vertices of a triangle and its orthocenter are each equal to the circumcircle of the triangle.
7. Prove Theorem 26 when angle C is obtuse.
8. Prove that the midpoint of a side of a triangle is equally distant from two vertices of its orthic triangle.
9. The three triangles cut from a triangle by the sides of the orthic triangle are each similar to the given triangle.
10. Prove that the circumcenter of the triangle ABC is the orthocenter of the triangle $A'B'C'$.
11. The triangles ABC, HBC, HCA, and HAB all have the same orthic triangle.
12. Prove that the medians of a triangle divide it into six equal parts.
13. The orthocenter of a triangle is the incenter or an excenter of its orthic triangle.

THEOREM 28.   *The medians of a triangle meet in a point which is two thirds of the distance from each vertex to the midpoint of the opposite side.*

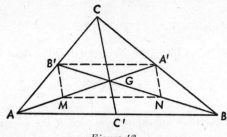

Figure 43

Prove that AA', BB', and CC' meet at G and that $AG = \frac{2}{3}AA'$.

Proof: AA' and BB' meet at some point G. M and N are the midpoints of AG and BG respectively.

Draw MN, NA', $A'B'$, and $B'M$.

In triangle ABG, MN is parallel to and equals half of AB.

In triangle ABC, $B'A'$ is parallel to and equals half of AB.

$\therefore MNA'B'$ is a parallelogram.   Therefore, $MG = GA'$ and $B'G = GN$.

Thus, $AG = \frac{2}{3}AA'$ and $BG = \frac{2}{3}BB'$.

The student should now prove that CC' passes through G and that $CG = \frac{2}{3}CC'$.

Definitions.   The point of intersection of the medians is called the *centroid* of the triangle.

The triangle formed by connecting the midpoints of the sides of a triangle is called the *medial triangle* of the given triangle.

THEOREM 29.   *The median drawn from any vertex of a triangle is less than half the sum of the sides including this angle.*   See Figure 44.

Prove that $CC' < \frac{1}{2}(CA + CB)$.

Proof: Extend CC' making $C'E = CC'$.

Draw BE.   Prove $\triangle EBC' \cong \triangle AC'C$.

Then $CE < CB + BE$, etc.

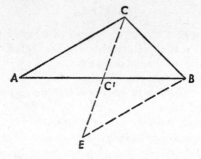

Figure 44

COROLLARY. *The sum of the medians of a triangle is less than the perimeter of the triangle.*

THEOREM 30. *The sum of the medians of a triangle is greater than three-fourths of the perimeter of the triangle.*

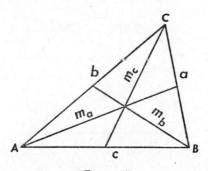

Figure 45

In the triangle ABC

$$\tfrac{2}{3}m_a + \tfrac{2}{3}m_b > c \qquad \text{also,} \qquad \tfrac{2}{3}m_a + \tfrac{2}{3}m_c > b$$

and

$$\tfrac{2}{3}m_c + \tfrac{2}{3}m_b > a.$$

Thus

$$\tfrac{4}{3}m_a + \tfrac{4}{3}m_b + \tfrac{4}{3}m_c > a + b + c$$

or

$$m_a + m_b + m_c > \tfrac{3}{4}a + \tfrac{3}{4}b + \tfrac{3}{4}c.$$

$$\therefore \ m_a + m_b + m_c > \tfrac{3}{4}(a + b + c).$$

EXERCISES

1. If two medians of a triangle are equal, it is isosceles.
2. If two sides of a triangle are unequal, the included median cannot be perpendicular to the opposite side.
3. Two triangles are congruent if they have a side, and the median and altitude to that side in one respectively equal to the corresponding parts of the other.
4. A triangle and its medial triangle are similar.
5. A triangle is four times as large as its medial triangle.
6. A triangle and its medial triangle have the same centroid.
7. In a right triangle the median from the vertex of the right angle is half the hypotenuse.
8. State and prove the converse of Exercise 7.

THEOREM 31. *In any triangle the segment of an altitude from a vertex to the orthocenter is twice the perpendicular from the circumcenter to the same side.*

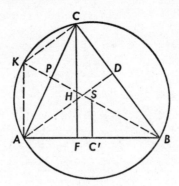

Figure 46

Let H be the orthocenter, and S the circumcenter.

Prove that $CH = 2SC'$.

SC' is $\parallel$ to KA and equal to half of it.   (Theorem 40, page 121.)

Then $CH \parallel KA$.

Since $\angle KCB$ is a right $\angle$, $KC \parallel AH$ and $AHCK$ is a parallelogram.

$$\therefore CH = KA = 2SC'.$$

EXERCISES

1. Prove that the four extremities of any two altitudes of a triangle are concyclic.
2. The product of the segments into which the orthocenter divides one altitude equals the product of the segments into which it divides any other altitude.
3. Explain the proof of Theorem 31 when C is a right angle.
4. Prove Theorem 31 when angle C is obtuse.

THEOREM 32. *The orthocenter, the centroid, and the circumcenter, are collinear.*

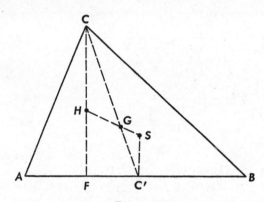

Figure 47

Connect the orthocenter (H) and the circumcenter (S) and prove that the intersection of HS with the median CC' is the centroid.

Proof: $CF \parallel SC'$.

$$\triangle GCH \sim \triangle GC'S$$
$$CH = 2SC' \qquad \therefore \ CG = 2GC'$$

and G is the centroid.

COROLLARY. *The centroid of a triangle is two-thirds of the distance from the orthocenter to the circumcenter.*

THEOREM 33.   (THE NINE-POINT CIRCLE.)   *A circle whose center is the midpoint of the segment joining the orthocenter and the circumcenter, and whose radius is equal to half the radius of the circumcircle, passes through the feet of the altitudes, the midpoints of the sides, and the midpoints of the segments joining the vertices of the triangle to the orthocenter.*

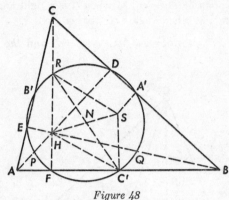

Figure 48

The $\triangle$ is lettered with the usual notation.   See page 40.

Draw HS and $C'R$ intersecting at N.

We will prove that N is the midpoint of HS and that a circle with N as center and a radius equal to $\frac{1}{2}CS$ will pass through D, E, F, A', B', C', P, Q, R.

1. $HR = \frac{1}{2}HC = C'S$.   Also $HR \parallel C'S$.
   $\therefore HC'SR$ is a parallelogram and $HN = NS$ and $C'N = NR$.
   Therefore N is the midpoint of HS.
2. Since $C'FR$ is a right angle, a circle with N as a center and with a radius of NR will pass through R, F, and C'.
3. CR and SC' are equal and parallel.   Therefore $CRC'S$ is a parallelogram and $C'R = SC$ (a circumradius).
   $\therefore NR = \frac{1}{2}C'R = \frac{1}{2}SC$.

We have proved that N is the midpoint of HS, that the circle with N as a center and one half of SC (a circumradius) as a radius passes through a foot of an altitude, F, a midpoint of a side, C', and a midpoint of CH, R.   Similarly the circle may be proved to pass through the other six points.

This circle is called the *nine-point circle* and its center, N, is the *nine-point center*.

COROLLARY.   *The orthocenter, the centroid, the circumcenter, and the nine-point center are collinear.*   This is called the *Euler line* of the triangle.

EXERCISES

1. The nine-point circle of a triangle ABC is also the nine-point circle of the triangles AHB, BHC, CHA, where H is the orthocenter.

2. All triangles that have the same orthocenter and the same circumcircle have the same nine-point circle.

3. Prove that the nine-point circle bisects any line from the orthocenter to a point on the circumcircle.

4. Test the proof of Theorem 32 for a right triangle.   What is the location of the points H, G, and S?

5. Give a complete proof of Theorem 32 when C is an obtuse angle.

6. In Figure 47, if C approaches nearer and nearer F along CF, and AB remains fixed, what is the locus of H? of G? of S?

7. Each median of a triangle is equidistant from two vertices.

8. If two sides of a triangle are unequal, the greater side has the smaller median drawn to it.

9. The perpendicular from the centroid of a triangle to any straight line not intersecting the triangle is equal to one-third the sum of the perpendiculars from the vertices of the triangle to the same line.

10. The angle formed by the median and altitude drawn from the vertex of the right angle of a right angle triangle to the hypotenuse equals the difference of the other two angles of the triangle.

11. Construct a triangle given a median and altitude to one side and another median (m_b, h_b, m_c).

12. Prove that the circumcenter of a triangle is the orthocenter of its medial triangle.

13. Prove that the lines joining the centroid to the vertices of a triangle divide the triangle into three equal parts.

14. Using the usual notation, prove that A is an excenter of triangle DEF.

15. If BE and CF are altitudes of triangle ABC, prove that the triangles AEF and ABC are similar.

Historical Note. The nine-point circle was discovered by Brianchon and Poncelet, French mathematicians, who published the proof in a joint paper in 1820. The theorem was discovered independently by other geometers.

THEOREM 34. (THE SIMSON LINE.*) *If from any point P on the circumcircle of the triangle ABC, perpendiculars PL, PM, and PN are drawn to the sides of the triangle, then LNM is a straight line.*

Draw *AP* and *PB*.
We need to prove that $\angle MNP + \angle PNL =$ st. $\angle$.

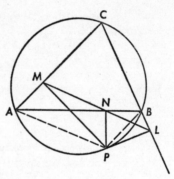

Figure 49

Since $\measuredangle\, AMP$ and ANP are rt. $\measuredangle$, $\therefore$ A, P, N, M are concyclic. (Theorem 14, Cor., page 33.)

Since $\measuredangle\, PNB$ and BLP are rt. $\measuredangle$, $\therefore$ P, L, B, N are concyclic. (Theorem 16, Cor., page 34.)

$\angle MNP = \angle CBP$, each being a supplement of $\angle PAM$. (Theorem 15, Cor., page 33.)

$\angle CBP$ is the supplement of $\angle PBL$.

But $\angle PBL = \angle PNL$ for $PLBN$ is a cyclic quadrilateral.

$\therefore$ $\angle MNP + \angle PNL =$ st. $\angle$ and MNL is a st. line.

This line is called the *Simson line* of the point P on the circumcircle.

* Due to Robert Simson (1687–1768), an English geometer.

THEOREM 35. (CEVA'S THEOREM.) *If three concurrent lines are drawn from the vertices A, B, C of the triangle ABC to meet the opposite sides in L, M, N, respectively, then*

$$\frac{BL}{LC} \cdot \frac{CM}{MA} \cdot \frac{AN}{NB} = 1.$$

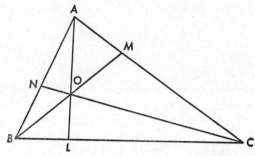

Figure 50

If O lies within the triangle, the three ratios are positive.

If O lies without the triangle, two of the ratios are negative and one is positive. Hence in any case the product of the three is positive.

$$\frac{BL}{LC} = \frac{\triangle BLA}{\triangle CLA} = \frac{\triangle BLO}{\triangle CLO} = \frac{\triangle BLA - \triangle BLO}{\triangle CLA - \triangle CLO}$$

$$= \frac{\triangle BOA}{\triangle COA}. \quad \text{(Theorem 86, page 123, and the laws of proportion.)}$$

Similarly
$$\frac{CM}{MA} = \frac{\triangle BOC}{\angle BOA},$$

and
$$\frac{AN}{NB} = \frac{\triangle COA}{\triangle BOC}.$$

$$\frac{BL}{LC} \cdot \frac{CM}{MA} \cdot \frac{AN}{NB} = \frac{\triangle BOA}{\triangle COA} \cdot \frac{\triangle BOC}{\triangle BOA} \cdot \frac{\triangle COA}{\triangle BOC}$$

or
$$\frac{BL}{LC} \cdot \frac{CM}{MA} \cdot \frac{AN}{NB} = 1.$$

Historical Note. Discovered by an Italian mathematician, Giovanni Ceva (1647-1736). It appeared in a work of Ceva's published in Milan in 1678.

THEOREM 36. (CONVERSE OF CEVA'S THEOREM.) *If three lines are drawn from the three vertices A, B, C, of the triangle ABC to the opposite sides meeting them in L, M, N, respectively, so that*

$$\frac{BL}{LC} \cdot \frac{CM}{MA} \cdot \frac{AN}{NB} = 1,$$

then the lines are concurrent.

Indirect proof.   Assume that two of the lines meet in O, and show that if the third does not pass through O an absurdity results.

EXERCISES

1. Prove Ceva's Theorem if O lies outside of the triangle.
2. Prove Ceva's Theorem if O lies (a) on a side of the triangle; (b) at a vertex.
3. What is the Simson line of a vertex of a triangle?
4. The Simson line of a point diametrically opposite a vertex is the side opposite that vertex.
5. Show that these theorems are corollaries to the converse of Ceva's Theorem:
   In any triangle these lines are concurrent:
   (a) The medians;   (b) The altitudes;
   (c) The bisectors of the interior angles;
   (d) The bisector of an interior angle and the bisectors of the exterior angles at the other vertices.
6. Lines drawn from the vertices of a triangle to the points of contact of the incircle with the opposite sides are concurrent.   This point of concurrence is called the *Gergonne point* of the triangle.
7. Lines drawn from the vertices of a triangle to the points of contact of the escribed circles with the opposite sides are concurrent.   This point of concurrence is called *Nagel's point* of the triangle.
8. In Figure 50, if NM is parallel to BC, then $BL = LC$.
9. In Figure 50, $\dfrac{OL}{AL} + \dfrac{OM}{BM} + \dfrac{ON}{CN} + 1.$

THEOREM 37. (MENELAUS' THEOREM.) *If a transversal cuts the three sides AB, BC, CA of the triangle ABC in the points L, M, N, respectively, then*

$$\frac{AL}{LB} \cdot \frac{BM}{MC} \cdot \frac{CN}{NA} = -1,$$

signs being taken into account.

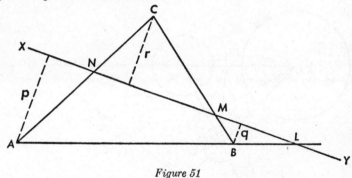

Figure 51

The transversal will cut but one or three of the sides externally, hence one or three of the ratios $\frac{AL}{LB}, \frac{BM}{MC}, \frac{CN}{NA}$ will be negative, and hence the product of the three ratios will always be negative.

Drop the three perpendiculars p, q, r, to the transversal XY.

From similar triangles, $\frac{AL}{LB} = -p/q, \frac{BM}{MC} = q/r, \frac{CN}{NA} = r/p.$

$\therefore \frac{AL}{LB} \cdot \frac{BM}{MC} \cdot \frac{CN}{NA} = -1$, signs being taken into account.

THEOREM 38. (CONVERSE OF MENELAUS' THEOREM.) *If the points L, M, N, are taken on the sides AB, BC, CA, respectively, of the triangle ABC, so that*

$$\frac{AL}{LB} \cdot \frac{BM}{MC} \cdot \frac{CN}{NA} = -1,$$

signs being taken into account, then L, M, N, are collinear.

Draw a line through two of the points and prove that unless it passes through the third an absurdity results.

THEOREM 39. *If three circles be taken two and two, forming three pairs, then (1) the lines joining the center of each circle and the internal center of similitude of the other two are concurrent; (2) the external centers of similitude of the three pairs are collinear; (3) the external center of similitude of any pair and the internal centers of similitude of the other two pairs are collinear.*

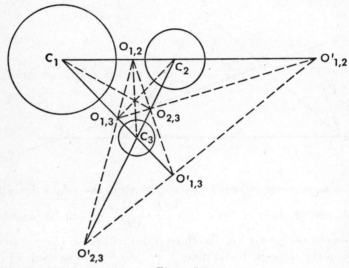

Figure 52

Let C_1, C_2, C_3 be the centers; $O_{1,2}$, $O'_{1,2}$ the internal and external centers of similitude of circles C_1, C_2; $O_{1,3}$, $O'_{1,3}$ the internal and external centers of similitude of circles C_1, C_3; and $O_{2,3}$, $O'_{2,3}$ the internal and external centers of similitude of circles C_2, C_3. Let r_1, r_2, r_3 be the radii of the three circles.

By applying the converse of Ceva's Theorem to $\triangle C_1C_2C_3$ prove (1). By applying the converse of Menelaus' Theorem to $\triangle C_1C_2C_3$ prove (2) and (3).

EXERCISES

1. Prove Menelaus' Theorem when the transversal cuts each side of the triangle externally.

2. The bisectors of two interior angles of a triangle and the bisector of the exterior angle at the third vertex intersect the sides of the triangle in collinear points.

3. The points in which the bisectors of the exterior angles of a triangle meet the opposite sides are collinear.

4. Consider Menelaus' Theorem when LMN (a) passes through a vertex, (b) bisects a side, (c) is parallel to a side, (d) perpendicular to a side.

5. In Figure 50, page 55, let a circle be passed through points L, M, and N, cutting BC again in L', CA in M', and AB in N'. Prove that AL', BM', and CN' are concurrent.

6. Let the circle inscribed in the triangle ABC touch BC in A', CA in B', and AB in C'. Prove that AA', BB', and CC' are concurrent.

7. The altitude from A of the triangle ABC meets the circumcircle in M. Prove that the Simson line of M is parallel to the tangent at A.

8. In the triangle ABC the bisectors of the angles B and C meet the opposite sides in W and J respectively and WJ meets BC in P. Prove that AP is a bisector of an exterior angle at A.

9. Construct a triangle given the three medians.

10. Construct a triangle given the feet of the three altitudes.

Historical Note. Theorem 37 was known to Menelaus (c. 100 B.C.). Credit for it was formerly given to Pappus (c. 300) whose works contain theorems dealing with the equality of the cross ratios cut from a pencil of four lines by two transversals.

Menelaus of Alexandria was an astronomer as well as a mathematician and made important contributions to spherical geometry, especially to the geometry of the spherical triangle. His treatise on spherics was translated into various languages, and many editions of it have appeared.

Menelaus' Theorem may be stated: Any line cuts the sides of a triangle so that the product of three non-adjacent segments equals the product of the other three.

Ceva's Theorem may be stated: If three concurrent lines are drawn, one from each vertex of a triangle, they divide the opposite sides so that the product of three non-adjacent segments equals the product of the other three.

A line from the vertex of a triangle to the opposite side is sometimes called a *cevian line*.

THEOREM 40.   (PASCAL'S THEOREM.)   *The points of intersection of the opposite sides of an inscribed hexagon are collinear.*

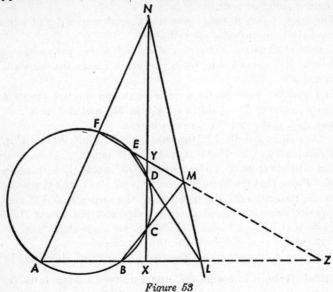

Figure 53

Prove L, M, N, collinear.

Consider the triangle XYZ whose vertices are the points of intersection of AB and CD, CD and EF, and EF and AB, respectively, and consider DE, FA and BC as transversals cutting the sides of $\triangle XYZ$.

By applying Menelaus' Theorem we have these three relations:

$$\frac{XL}{LZ} \cdot \frac{ZE}{EY} \cdot \frac{YD}{DX} = -1; \qquad \frac{YN}{NX} \cdot \frac{XA}{AZ} \cdot \frac{ZF}{FY} = -1;$$

$$\frac{ZM}{MY} \cdot \frac{YC}{CX} \cdot \frac{XB}{BZ} = -1.$$

Taking the products of the three right members and the three left members of these three equalities, and rearranging the ratios,

$$\frac{XL}{LZ} \cdot \frac{ZM}{MY} \cdot \frac{YN}{NX} \cdot \frac{ZE \cdot ZF}{ZB \cdot ZA} \cdot \frac{XB \cdot XA}{XC \cdot XD} \cdot \frac{YC \cdot YD}{YE \cdot YF} = -1.$$

Now each of the three last fractions in this product equals 1 (Theorem 4, page 19).

$$\therefore \frac{XL}{LZ} \cdot \frac{ZM}{MY} \cdot \frac{YN}{NX} = -1$$

$\therefore$ L, M, N are collinear. (Theorem 38, page 57.)

COROLLARY 1. *If six points A, B, C, D, E, F, on a circle be joined in any order, by six consecutive straight lines forming a closed figure ABCDEFA, Pascal's Theorem still applies.* Such a figure as Figure 54 is called a *hexagram*.

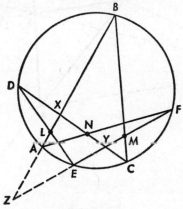

Figure 54

COROLLARY 2. *If in the hexagon ABCDEF, the vertex B be made to approach nearer and nearer A, the side AB will approach a tangent at A; similarly D may be made to approach C, and F approach E, side CD a tangent at C, and side EF a tangent at E.* Show that Pascal's theorem then takes this form: *In an inscribed triangle the intersections of each side with the tangent through the opposite vertex are collinear.*

This is an example of the use of the Principle of Continuity.

EXERCISE

1. Consider Pascal's Theorem for a regular hexagon.

THEOREM 41. (DESARGUES' THEOREM.)   *If the triangles ABC and A'B'C' are so situated that AA', BB', and CC' are concurrent at O; and if BC and B'C' meet in L, CA and C'A' meet in M, and AB and A'B' meet in N, then L, M, and N are collinear, and conversely.*

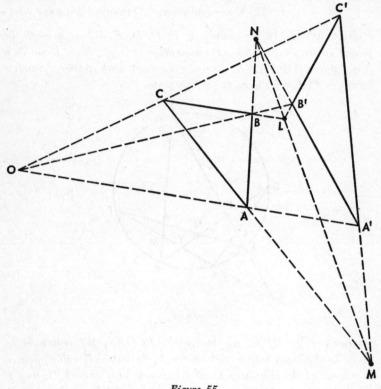

Figure 55

Prove that $\dfrac{AN}{NB} \cdot \dfrac{BL}{LC} \cdot \dfrac{CM}{MA} = -1$, by using the transversals $LB'C'$, $MC'A'$, $NA'B'$ of the sides of the triangles OBC, OCA, OAB, respectively.

Consider the position of line NLM in figure 55, when the two triangles are homothetic.

Historical Note. Gerard Desargues (1593–1662), was an engineer and architect but later gave his time to geometry and its applications. Besides enunciating this theorem, which is basic in modern projective geometry, he opened up new fields in geometry by the introduction of points and lines at infinity. The work of Desargues and his contemporaries started the first advance in Geometry since the time of the ancient Greeks.

EXERCISES

1. Given the orthocenter, the center of the nine-point circle, and the midpoint of the base, to construct the triangle.
2. Given the base c and the vertical angle of a triangle. Trace the locus of the center of the nine-point circle as C traces its locus.
3. What is the locus of a point which moves so that if perpendiculars are drawn from it to the sides of a given triangle the feet of these perpendiculars are collinear?
4. The triangles ABC and $AB'C'$ have a common vertical angle and the circles circumscribed about them meet at P. Shown that the feet of the perpendiculars from P to the four lines AB, AC, BC, $B'C'$ are collinear.
5. If in Figure 50, page 55, $BL = \frac{1}{4}BC$ and $CM = \frac{2}{3}CA$, for what value of $\dfrac{AN}{NB}$ will AL, BM and CN be concurrent?
6. In the triangle ABC, AD, BE and CF are cevian lines concurrent at O.
   Prove that $\dfrac{OE}{BE} + \dfrac{OD}{AD} + \dfrac{OF}{CF} = 1.$
   Test this theorem with the medians of a triangle.

Historical Note. Blaise Pascal (1623–1662), French philosopher, mathematician, physicist, and inventor. At the age of sixteen he wrote a remarkable paper on cones, which contained Theorem 40, page 60, and at nineteen had invented a calculating machine. He called attention to the triangular arrangement of the coefficients of the powers of a binomial, called Pascal's triangle. He also helped to lay the foundation of the theory of probability and developed the theory of the cycloid.

MODERN GEOMETRY

The ancient Greeks were the first to make geometry a science. The two outstanding treatises on geometry, the *Elements* of Euclid and the treatise on conics by Apollonius, dominated the science for centuries.

Since the Greeks, the first decided advance in geometry came about the beginning of the seventeenth century. This advance was in two lines: analytic, led by Rene Descartes (1596–1650); and synthetic, based on the principles of perspective and the theory of transversals. Desargues and Pascal were leaders in this development which came to fruition a century and a half later in the Projective Geometry of Poncelet (see page 112) and the Descriptive Geometry of Gaspard Monge (1746–1818).

The theorems so far discussed in this text go back to the ancient Greeks, except those theorems which have been accredited to more recent geometers. The remainder of the text deals in the main with modern geometry. It will be pointed out, however, that some of the ideas and methods of modern geometry had their genesis with ancient geometers.

CHAPTER 6

Harmonic Ranges and
Pencils

Definition.   A system of points on a straight line is called a *range.*

Definition.   If a straight line AB is divided by the two points C
and D so that $\dfrac{AC}{CB} \Big/ \dfrac{AD}{DB} = -1$, then AB is said to be *divided
harmonically.*   Then A, C, B, D are said to form a *harmonic range,*

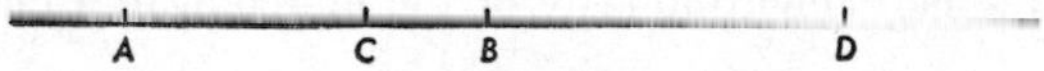

Figure 56

and C and D are called *harmonic conjugates* of each other with
respect to A and B.

   This definition is equivalent to the following, usually given in
elementary geometry: *If a straight line is divided internally and
externally in the same ratio, it is said to be divided harmonically.*

   The ratio $\dfrac{AC}{CB} \Big/ \dfrac{AD}{DB}$ is usually written $\{AB, CD\}$.

   COROLLARY.   *If AB is divided harmonically by C and D, then
CD is divided harmonically by A and B.*

EXERCISES

1. Review Theorems 102 and 103, page 125.
2. In the triangle ABC, BC is 8 in., CA is 6 in. and AB is 12 in; CD
   bisects angle C. Find the lengths of the parts into which AB is
   divided.

3. A line drawn through the vertex of a triangle, dividing the opposite
   side into segments proportional to the other two sides, bisects the
   angle.

4. Construct a triangle having given two sides and the shorter segment
   into which the bisector of their included angle divides the opposite
   side.

5. Take a line AB 6 in. long.   Divide it at C so that $AC/CB = 2$.
   Compute AD and locate D so that C and D divide AB harmonically.

6. Solve Exercise 5 if (a) $AC/CB = \frac{1}{2}$; (b) $AC/CB = -2$; (c)
   $AC/CB = -\frac{1}{2}$.

7. Suppose that AB is k units long, and is divided by C so that
   $\dfrac{AC}{CB} = \dfrac{m}{n}$. If C and D divide AB harmonically, show that $AD = \dfrac{mk}{m-n}$.

8. In Exercise 7 suppose that m and n are both positive.   Where is D
   located if (a) $m > n$?   (b) $m < n$?   (c) $m = n$?   Where are C and
   D located if $m = 0$?   If $n = 0$?

9. Let $\{AB,CD\} = -1$.   Describe the motion of D as C starts at A
   and moves to B.

10. What is the harmonic conjugate of the midpoint of a line segment
    AB?

11. Prove that the bisector of an angle of a triangle and the bisector
    of the adjacent exterior angle divide the side opposite harmonically.

12. Where does the bisector of the exterior angle at the vertex of an
    isosceles triangle meet the opposite side?

13. If $\{AB, CD\} = -1$, what is the position of D if C coincides (a) with
    A?   (b) with the midpoint of AB?   (c) with B?   (d) with the
    point at infinity on the line AB?

14. Divide a line AB 4 in. long harmonically if $\dfrac{AC}{CB} = \frac{3}{4}$.   Use Problems
    1 and 2, page 18.

15. Solve Exercise 14 by constructing a triangle having two of its sides
    in the ratio of 3/4.

16. The bisector of the angle A of a triangle ABC meets BC in X.
    Prove that AX is divided harmonically by the perpendiculars drawn
    to it from B and C.

17. The bisector of angle A of triangle ABC meets BC in T.   Construct
    the harmonic conjugate of T.

THEOREM 42. *If $\{AB, CD\} = -1$, then $\dfrac{1}{AC} + \dfrac{1}{AD} = \dfrac{2}{AB}$.*

Figure 57

Proof:

$$\frac{AC}{CB} = \frac{-AD}{DB}. \qquad \text{(Definition)}$$

$$\frac{CB}{AC} = \frac{BD}{AD}. \qquad \text{(Inversion and } BD = -DB.\text{)}$$

$$\frac{AB - AC}{AC} = \frac{AD - AB}{AD}. \qquad \text{(From the figure.)}$$

$$\frac{AB}{AC} - 1 = 1 - \frac{AB}{AD}.$$

$$\frac{AB}{AC} + \frac{AB}{AD} = 2.$$

$$\frac{1}{AC} + \frac{1}{AD} = \frac{2}{AB}.$$

Note. It follows from the above proof that

$$\frac{1}{AC}, \frac{1}{AB}, \frac{1}{AD}$$

are in arithmetic progression. Hence AC, AB, and AD are in harmonic progression. Hence the names harmonic range, and harmonic division.

EXERCISES

1. Prove the converse of Theorem 42.
2. If $\{AB, CD\} = -1$, then

   (a) $\dfrac{2}{BA} = \dfrac{1}{BC} + \dfrac{1}{BD}$; (b) $\dfrac{2}{CD} = \dfrac{1}{CA} + \dfrac{1}{CB}$; (c) $\dfrac{2}{DC} = \dfrac{1}{DA} + \dfrac{1}{DB}$.

3. Prove the converse of each part of the preceding exercise.

PROBLEM 4: *If A, C, B, is a range of points, to construct the harmonic conjugate of C with respect to A, B.*

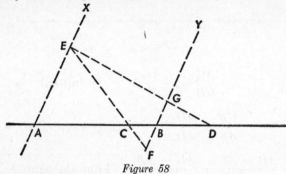

Figure 58

Solution: Through A and B, draw parallel lines AX and BY, and through C draw a transversal cutting AX in E and BY in F. Make $BG = BF$, and draw EG to cut the line AB in D.

Then D is the harmonic conjugate of C.
For $AC/CB = AE/BF$

$$= AE/BG$$

$$= AD/BD$$

$$= -AD/DB, \text{ signs being taken into account.}$$

EXERCISES

1. Divide a line AB harmonically in the ratio of two given lines m and n.
2. If through the vertex C of a triangle ABC a line CD is drawn parallel to AB and any point M in CD is joined to N the midpoint of AB, then MN is divided harmonically by BC and AC extended.
3. If a transversal cuts two intersecting lines and the bisectors of their angles, a harmonic range is formed. Interpret this theorem when the transversal is parallel to one of the given lines.

THEOREM 43. *If AB is divided harmonically at C and D, and if O is the midpoint of AB, then $OC \cdot OD = \overline{OB}^2$.*

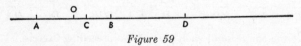

Figure 59

Proof:
$$\frac{AC}{CB} = \frac{-AD}{DB}.$$

$$AC \cdot BD = AD \cdot CB.$$

$$(AO + OC)(OD - OB) = (AO + OD)(OB - OC)$$

(from the figure).

$$(OB + OC)(OD - OB) = (OB + OD)(OB - OC)$$

(since $OB = AO$).

$$OB \cdot OD - \overline{OB}^2 + OC \cdot OD - OB \cdot OC$$
$$= \overline{OB}^2 - OB \cdot OC + OB \cdot OD - OC \cdot OD.$$

$$2OC \cdot OD = 2\overline{OB}^2.$$

$$OC \cdot OD = \overline{OB}^2.$$

Note: If we solve $OC \cdot OD = \overline{OB}^2$ for OD, we have $OD = \overline{OB}^2/OC$. Now if C approaches O, OD becomes infinite and D becomes the point at infinity on the line AB. Hence we say that the harmonic conjugate of the midpoint of a line segment AB with respect to its end points is the point at infinity on the line AB.

THEOREM 44. *If O is the midpoint of AB, and if $OC \cdot OD = \overline{OB}^2$, then $\{AB, CD\} = -1$.*

This is the converse of the previous theorem. Show that the present theorem may be proved by reversing the order of the steps of the proof of the previous theorem.

EXERCISE

C and D divide the diameter of a circle harmonically, C' and D' divide another diameter of the circle harmonically. Prove that C, D, C', and D' are concyclic points.

Definitions. A system of lines through a point is called a *pencil of lines* and the point is called the *vertex* of the pencil.

A straight line that cuts the lines of a *pencil* is called a *transversal* of the pencil.

If a transversal of a pencil of four lines cuts them in a harmonic range, the transversal is said to be *divided harmonically* by the pencil.

THEOREM 45.   *If a pencil of four lines cuts a harmonic range from a transversal, and if through one point of the range a parallel is drawn to one line of the pencil, the other three lines of the pencil cut two equal segments from this parallel.*

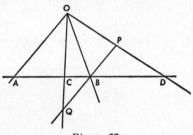

Figure 60

Proof: Let O be the vertex of the pencil, AD the transversal, and $PQ \parallel OA$.

We are to prove that $PB = BQ$.

$$\frac{AC}{CB} = \frac{AD}{-DB} = \frac{AD}{BD}.$$

$$\frac{AC}{CB} = \frac{OA}{BQ}, \text{ since } \triangle ACO \sim \triangle BCQ.$$

$$\frac{AD}{BD} = \frac{OA}{PB}, \text{ since } \triangle ADO \sim \triangle BDP.$$

$$\therefore \frac{OA}{PB} = \frac{OA}{BQ}.$$

$$\therefore PB = BQ.$$

THEOREM 46.   *If from a point B on one line of a pencil of four lines, a line be drawn parallel to another line of the pencil, and if the other three lines of the pencil cut off two equal segments on this parallel, the pencil cuts off a harmonic range from every line through B.*

This is a converse of the previous theorem.   Prove it by reversing the proof of the previous theorem.

THEOREM 47. *If a pencil of four lines divides one transversal harmonically, it divides every other transversal harmonically.*

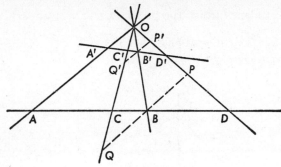

Figure 61

Proof: Let O be the vertex of the pencil, $\{AB, CD\} = -1$, $A'D'$ any transversal, and draw PQ through B and $P'Q'$ through B' both parallel to OA.

$$\frac{AC}{CB} = -\frac{AD}{DB}.$$

$$\therefore PB - BQ. \quad \text{(Theorem 45, page 70.)}$$

$$\frac{PB}{P'B'} = \frac{OB}{OB'} = \frac{BQ}{B'Q'},$$

since $\triangle OPB \sim \triangle OP'B'$, and $\triangle OBQ \sim \triangle OB'Q'$.

$$\therefore P'B' = B'Q'.$$

$$\therefore \{A'B', C'D'\} = -1. \quad \text{(Theorem 46, page 70.)}$$

This is a fundamental theorem of Projective Geometry.

Definitions. If a pencil of four lines divides a transversal harmonically, the pencil is called a *harmonic pencil.*

It follows from Theorem 47, above, that a harmonic pencil divides every transversal harmonically. If the pencil $OA, OB, OC,$ OD, is harmonic, then OC and OD are called *harmonic conjugates* of each other with respect to OA and OB.

We write $O\{AB, CD\} = -1$ to indicate that the pencil $OA,$ OB, OC, OD is harmonic.

THEOREM 48. *The bisectors of the adjacent angles formed by two intersecting lines are harmonic conjugates with respect to the two lines.*

Let the student furnish the proof.

PROBLEM 5: *Given a pencil of lines OA, OB, OC, to construct the harmonic conjugate of OC with respect to OA, OB.*

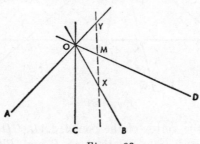

Figure 62

Solution: Through X on OB draw a parallel to OC cutting OA in Y.   Through the midpoint M of XY draw OD.

Then $O\{AB, CD\} = -1$.

Show that XY cuts a harmonic range from the pencil $O\{AB, CD\}$.

THEOREM 49. *If $\{AB, CD\}$ and $\{A'B', C'D'\}$ are any two harmonic ranges, and if AA', BB', and CC' are concurrent, then DD' passes through the point of concurrence.*

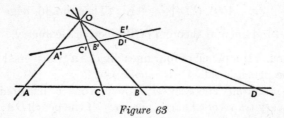

Figure 63

Proof: Let O be the point of concurrence of AA', BB', and CC'.

Suppose that DD' does not pass through O, and that OD cuts $A'D'$ at E'.

Then $\dfrac{AC}{CB} \Big/ \dfrac{AD}{DB} = \dfrac{A'C'}{C'B'} \Big/ \dfrac{A'D'}{D'B'}$ (Given).

$$= \dfrac{A'C'}{C'B'} \Big/ \dfrac{A'E'}{E'B'} \quad \text{(Theorem 47, page 71).}$$

Then $\qquad \dfrac{A'C' \cdot D'B'}{C'B' \cdot A'D'} = \dfrac{A'C' \cdot E'B'}{C'B' \cdot A'E'} \cdot$

$\therefore \dfrac{D'B'}{A'D'} = \dfrac{E'B'}{A'E'}$ or $\dfrac{A'D'}{D'B'} = \dfrac{A'E'}{E'B'} \cdot$

$\therefore E'$ coincides with D'. (Theorem 1, page 8.)

$\therefore DD'$ passes through O.

THEOREM 50. *If two harmonic ranges $\{AB, CD\}$ and $\{A'B', C'D'\}$ have a point A in common, then BB', CC', and DD' are concurrent.*

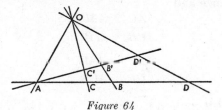

Figure 64

Let the student show that this is a particular case of the previous theorem.

EXERCISES

1. A chord MN is perpendicular to a diameter RS. If P is any other point on the circle, $P\{MN, RS\}$ is a harmonic pencil.
2. From a point T two tangents TP and TQ are drawn to a circle. AB is a diameter of the circle and QS is drawn perpendicular to AB. Prove that $Q\{TS, BA\}$ is harmonic.
3. A, B, C, D, E, F are six points on a circle. If $E\{AB, CD\}$ is harmonic, prove that $F\{AB, CD\}$ is harmonic.
4. Two circles intersect at B and C. A common tangent touches them at P and Q and another circle through B and C at L and M. Prove that $\{PQ, LM\}$ is harmonic.

THEOREM 51. *If $O\{AB, CD\}$ and $O'\{AB, CD\}$ are two harmonic pencils and if A, B, C are collinear, then D is on the line ABC.*

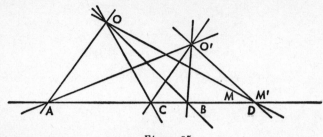

Figure 65

Suppose that OD and $O'D$ do not meet on ABC, but cut ABC in M and M' respectively.

Since $O\{AB, CM\}$ is a harmonic pencil, therefore $\{AB, CM\}$ is a harmonic range and

$$\frac{AC}{CB} = \frac{AM}{MB}$$

and similarly

$$\frac{AC}{CB} = \frac{AM'}{M'B}.$$

$\therefore \dfrac{AM}{MB} = \dfrac{AM'}{M'B}$ and M and M' coincide by Theorem 1, page 8.

THEOREM 52. *If $O\{AB, CD\}$ and $O'\{AB, CD\}$ are harmonic, and if O' lies on OD, then A, B, C are collinear.*

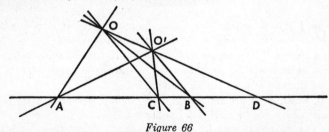

Figure 66

Let the student show that this is a particular case of Theorem 51.

EXERCISES

1. If two lines of a harmonic pencil are orthogonal (perpendicular), these lines are the bisectors of the angles formed by the other two lines.
2. A necessary and sufficient condition that a pencil of four lines be harmonic is that a parallel to one of the lines be divided into two equal parts by the other three.
3. Construct the harmonic conjugate of one line of a pencil of three lines with respect to the other two.
4. What is the harmonic conjugate of the median to one side of a triangle with respect to the other two sides?
5. One altitude of a triangle and the side to which it is drawn are harmonic conjugates with respect to the two sides of the pedal triangle drawn from the foot of that altitude.
6. A harmonic pencil is formed by one side of a triangle, the median to that side, and the lines joining the midpoint of that side to the midpoints of the other two sides.
7. The tangent at any point on a circle and the perpendicular from that point to a diameter divide that diameter harmonically.
8. ABC is an inscribed $\triangle$, DE is a diameter $\perp$ to AC. If DB and EB are drawn and produced to meet the base AC (extended, if necessary), they divide it harmonically.

   Suggestion. Prove that DB and EB are the bisectors of the interior and exterior angles of the triangle.
9. The diameter of a circle that is perpendicular to one of the sides of an inscribed triangle is divided harmonically by the other two sides.
10. In a harmonic pencil if one line bisects the angle between the other pair of lines, it is perpendicular to its conjugate line.

CHAPTER 7 Inversion

Definitions. If on the line OP the point P' be taken so that $OP \cdot OP' = k^2$, then P and P' are said to be *inverse* to each other with respect to the circle with center O and radius k. O is called the *center of inversion* and k the *radius of inversion*, or the *constant of inversion*. The operation of obtaining one of the points when the other is given is called *inversion*.

It is evident that OP and OP' vary inversely, which gives rise to the name. The figure formed by the inverses of the points of a given figure is called the *inverse of the given figure*.

PROBLEM 6. *To construct the inverse of a point.*

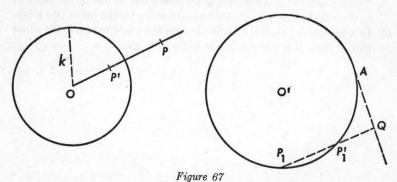

Figure 67

Given a circle of radius k and center O, and a point P, to construct the inverse of P with respect to the circle.

Construction: Draw a circle with any center, as O', and with any convenient radius. At a point A on this circle construct a tangent. Mark off on the tangent a length $AQ = k$. With Q as center and radius OP strike an arc cutting the circle at P_1. Draw QP_1, and let P_1' be the other point of intersection of QP_1 with the circle. With O as center and QP_1 as radius strike an arc cutting OP at P'. Then P' is the inverse of P.

Proof: $QP_1 \cdot QP_1' = \overline{QA}^2$. Why?
   Then $OP \cdot OP' = k^2$. Why?

EXERCISES

1. Take a center of inversion O and a radius of inversion 2 inches. Find the inverse, P', of P if P is 4 inches from the center. What is the length of OP'?

2. With the same center and radius of inversion as in Exercise 1, find the inverse of Q, if $OQ = \frac{3}{4}$ inch. Find the length of OQ'.

3. Take a center of inversion O and a radius of inversion of 2 inches. Draw a straight line 4 inches from O. Find the inverses of several points on the line. Do you get any suggestions from your drawing as to what the locus of these inverses is?

4. With any convenient radius of inversion find the inverses of several points on a line through the center of inversion. What is the inverse of this line?

5. With a center of inversion O and a radius of inversion 2 inches find the inverses of several points on a circle with center O and radius 4 inches. What is the inverse of this circle?

6. With a center of inversion O and a radius of inversion of 2 inches find the inverses of several points on a circle of radius 1 inch and with its center 3 inches from O. What do you think the inverse of this circle is?

7. Show that every point in the plane, except the center of inversion, has for a given radius of inversion one and only one inverse.

8. Show that the inverse of a point on the circle of inversion is the point itself, and conversely, if a point is its own inverse it lies on the circle of inversion.

9. What is the inverse of the circle of inversion?

10. If P and P' are inverses with respect to a circle whose center is O, what is the location of P' as P approaches as nearly as we please to O?

11. Does the center of the circle of inversion have an inverse? If so, where is it?
12. What is the inverse of the line at infinity with respect to a given circle of inversion?
13. Let a variable circle C', concentric with and inside the circle of inversion, continually grow smaller. What becomes of the inverse of C' as its radius becomes nearer and nearer zero?

THEOREM 53. *If a point P is outside the circle of inversion O, its inverse P' is the intersection of OP with the chord joining the points of contact of the tangents drawn to the circle of inversion from P.*

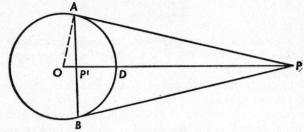

Figure 68

Draw OA and prove the triangles $OP'A$ and OPA similar.

Then $OP : OA = OA : OP'$ or $OP \cdot OP' = \overline{CA}^2$ and P' is the inverse of P.

THEOREM 54. *Conversely, if P is inside the circle, the tangents at the extremeties of the chord AB, which is perpendicular to OP at P, meet OP extended at P' the inverse of P.*

Let the student prove it.

EXERCISES

1. In Figure 68 if OP remains a constant and revolves about O as a center, what is the locus of P'? State your conclusions as a theorem and prove it.
2. Prove that for a given center and a given radius of inversion two pairs of inverse points are concyclic. (Apply Theorem 5, page 20.)
3. What is the locus of the inverse of the midpoint of the radius of inversion as the radius makes a complete revolution about the center of inversion?

4. Circumscribe a square about the circle of inversion and prove that the inverses of its vertices and points of tangency lie on the sides of an inscribed square. Do the inverses of other points on the circumscribed square lie on the sides of this inscribed square?

THEOREM 55. *The inverse of a straight line through the center of inversion is the line itself.*

Let the student show that the proof follows at once from the definition.

THEOREM 56. *The inverse of a straight line not passing through the center of inversion is a circle through the center of inversion.*

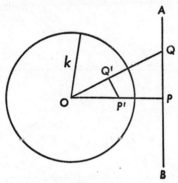

Figure 69

Let O be the center and k the radius of inversion. Let OP be perpendicular to the given line AB and let P' be the inverse of P and Q' the inverse of any other point Q on AB.

Then $OP \cdot OP' = OQ \cdot OQ' = k^2$

$$\therefore \frac{OP}{OQ} = \frac{OQ'}{OP'}$$

$$\therefore \triangle OPQ \sim \triangle OQ'P'$$

$$\therefore \angle Q' = \angle P = \text{rt. } \angle.$$

Hence, since O and P' are fixed points, the locus of Q' as Q traces out the line AB is the circle with OP' as diameter (Theorem 14, Cor., page 33).

EXERCISES

1. Given the center of inversion O and a point and its inverse on a line through O, find the radius of inversion.
2. The inverse of a straight line (not a diameter) which intersects the circle of inversion is determined by what three points?
3. Explain how we may consider Theorem 55 a special case of Theorem 56.

THEOREM 57. *The inverse of a circle not passing through the center of inversion is a circle.*

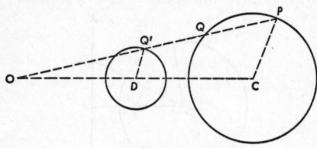

Figure 70

Let O be the center of inversion, C the center of the given circle, and OP the line from the center of inversion to any point P on the given circle. Let Q be the other point of intersection of OP with the given circle, and Q' be the inverse of Q. Connect C and P and draw $Q'D \parallel PC$.

Then $OQ \cdot OQ' = $ a constant. (What does it equal?)

Also, $OQ \cdot OP = $ a constant. (Theorem 4, page 19.)

$\therefore OP/OQ' = $ a constant. Why?

$OC/OD = OP/OQ'$, from similar triangles.

Since $OC = $ a constant, $OD = $ a constant, and D is a fixed point, and $DQ'/CP = OD/OC$.

$\therefore DQ' = $ a constant.

$\therefore$ The locus of Q' as Q traces out the circle is a circle with center D and radius DQ'. (Theorem 13, page 31.)

The theorem is then proved.

THEOREM 58. *The inverse of a circle passing through the center of inversion is a straight line perpendicular to the diameter through the center of inversion.*

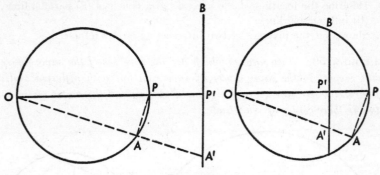

Figure 71

Let O be the center of inversion, k the radius of inversion, OP a diameter of the given circle, P' the inverse of P, and BP' perpendicular to OP.   Draw any other line OA intersecting the circle in A and BP' in A'.

We shall need to prove that A' is the inverse of A.

Proof:

$\angle PAO$ is a rt. angle. $\therefore$ $\angle A'AP$ is a rt. angle.

Also $\angle OP'A'$ is a rt. angle. $\therefore$ $AA'P'P$ is a cyclic quadrilateral and $OA \cdot OA' = OP \cdot OP' = k^2$.   (Theorem 4, page 19.)

$\therefore$ A' is the inverse of A and BP' is the inverse of the circle OAP.

EXERCISES

1. Find the radius and construct the circle of inversion in Figure 70.
2. What is the inverse of a circle whose center is the center of inversion and whose radius is (a) $1/\sqrt{2}$ times the radius of inversion?   (b) $\sqrt{2}$ times the radius of inversion?
3. Find the radius of the inverse of a circle externally tangent to the circle of inversion and equal to it.
4. Given O the circle of inversion and O' an externally tangent circle. Describe the position and magnitude of the inverse of O', as O' becomes (a) larger and larger, (b) smaller and smaller.

EXERCISES

1. What are the inverses of all equal circles that can be drawn through the center of inversion?
2. Describe the location of the inverses of a pencil of (a) parallel lines, (b) intersecting lines.
3. Show that the inverses of two intersecting circles intersect.

THEOREM 59.   *Two figures which are the inverses of the same figure with respect to the same center of inversion but with different radii of inversion are similar and similarly placed, and the center of inversion is their center of similitude.*

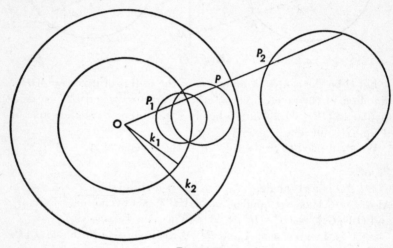

Figure 72

Proof: Let O be the center of inversion and P any point on the given figure.   Let P_1 and P_2 be the inverses of P when k_1 and k_2 are taken as the radii of inversion.

Then $OP \cdot OP_1 = k_1{}^2$ and $OP \cdot OP_2 = k_2{}^2$.

Then $OP_1 : OP_2 = k_1{}^2 : k_2{}^2$.

The theorem is then proved.

Note.   It follows that the radius of inversion does not affect the shape of the inverse figure.   Since in most problems of inversion we wish to determine only the shape of the inverse figure, no reference is made to the radius or the circle of inversion, and we speak of inversion with reference to a point, the center of inversion.

EXERCISES

Answer without giving proofs.

1. What is the inverse of a square (a) with respect to a vertex? (b) with respect to the midpoint of a side?
2. What is the inverse of a parallelogram with respect to (a) a vertex? (b) the intersection of its diagonals? (c) any point?

THEOREM 60. *If $PMP'N$ is a rhombus, and $OM = ON$, then P and P' are inverse points with respect to O for all positions of P.*

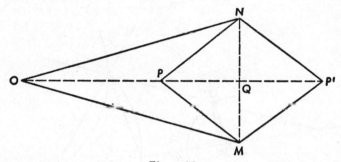

Figure 73

Proof: Since OP and OP' both bisect $\angle O$, then OPP' is a straight line.   Let Q be the point of intersection of the diagonals of $PMP'N$.

Then $OP \cdot OP' = (OQ - PQ)(OQ + PQ)$

$$= \overline{OQ}^2 - \overline{PQ}^2$$

$$= \overline{ON}^2 - \overline{QN}^2 - (\overline{PN}^2 - \overline{QN}^2)$$

$$= \overline{ON}^2 - \overline{PN}^2 = \text{a constant.}$$

The theorem is then proved.

COROLLARY. *If O is a fixed point and P traces a circle passing through O, the locus of P' is a straight line.*

Historical Note. If a model of Figure 73 be made by joining six rigid rods so that they move freely about their junction-points O, P, M, P', and N, we have an apparatus known as Peaucellier's Cell. It was invented about 1870 by Peaucellier, a captain in the French army who " won, although he did not at once receive, the Montyon prize from the French Academy by solving an ancient problem of imparting rectilinear motion to a point without guiding edge of any kind." Such an apparatus is known as a *linkage*. Such a device enables us to draw a straight line without a straight edge. It also gives us a device for drawing the inverse of any curve. For if O is a fixed point and P traces a given curve, then P' describes its inverse curve.

THEOREM 61. *Two intersecting curves cut at the same angles as their inverses.*

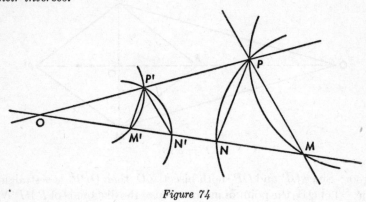

Figure 74

Proof: Let PN and PM be secants of the given curves which intersect at P; and let P', M', and N' be the inverses of P, M, and N, respectively. Draw secants $P'M'$ and $P'N'$.

Since $\triangle OP'N' \sim \triangle ONP$, $\angle OP'N' = \angle ONP$.
Since $\triangle OP'M' \sim \triangle OMP$, $\angle OP'M' = \angle OMP$.
$\therefore \angle OP'N' - \angle OP'M' = \angle ONP - \angle OMP$.
$\therefore \angle M'P'N' = \angle NPM$.

That is, the angle between the secants PM and PN equals the angle between the secants $P'M'$ and $P'N'$.

Now let M and N approach P. Then the secants through P and P' will approach the tangents at P and P' respectively. Therefore the angle between the tangents at P equals the angle between the tangents at P'. Hence the given curves intersect at the same angles as their inverses.

Here again we use the Principle of Continuity. State it.

EXERCISES

1. A harmonic range on a line m inverts into a harmonic range when the center of inversion is on m.
2. If two points are inverse to each other with respect to a given circle they divide harmonically the diameter on which they lie.
3. If a circle C divides one diameter of a circle C' harmonically it divides every other diameter of C' which meets it harmonically.
4. A family of circles through a given point may be inverted into a family of straight lines.
5. A family of circles all tangent at the same point may be inverted into a family of parallel lines.
6. Is it possible to invert a circle into itself when the center of inversion is (a) within the circle; (b) on the circle; (c) outside the circle?
7. Tangent circles invert into tangent circles.
8. What is the inverse of a square with respect to its inscribed circle? With respect to its circumscribed circle?
9. Answer the same questions concerning an equilateral triangle.
10. A family of circles pass through P and Q. What is the inverse of the family with respect to the midpoint of PQ, when $k = \dfrac{PQ}{2}$?
11. What is the inverse of a rectangle with respect to its center?
12. The inverse circles of a system of parallel lines are tangent at the center of inversion.
13. In Figure 69, page 79, describe the size and position of the inverse circle of AB when (a) AB is tangent to the circle of inversion; (b) AB is $\frac{1}{2}k$ distant from O; (c) AB is $2k$ distant from O; (d) AB moves farther and farther away from O; (e) AB gets nearer and nearer to O; (f) AB passes through O.
14. What is the inverse of a family of circles intersecting at A and B with respect to A?
15. What is the inverse of a plane with respect to any point (a) in it? (b) outside of it?

CHAPTER 8 Pole and Polar

Definitions. The *polar* of a point P with respect to a circle with center O is the line perpendicular to OP through the inverse of P with respect to the circle. P is called the *pole* of its polar.

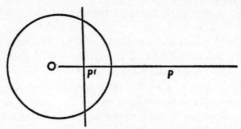

Figure 75

COROLLARY. *If the polar of a point P with respect to a circle of center O and radius r cuts OP in P', then $OP' \cdot OP = r^2$.*

EXERCISES

1. What is the polar with respect to a given circle of: (a) a point on the circle? (b) the center of the circle? (c) a point at infinity?
2. What is the pole of: (a) a tangent to the circle? (b) a diameter? (c) the line at infinity?
3. The polar of a point outside a circle is the chord of contact of the tangents from the point to the circle.
4. What is the pole of a secant to a circle? Prove your answer.
5. What are the polars of the vertices of a triangle with respect to (a) its inscribed circle? (b) its circumscribed circle?

THEOREM 62. *A line passing through a point and cutting a circle is divided harmonically by the circle, the point, and the polar of the point with respect to the circle.*

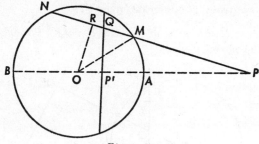

Figure 76

Proof: Let QP' be the polar of P with respect to the circle.

Let PN be any secant cutting the circle in N and M and the polar of P in Q. Draw $OR \perp PN$.

Then, since R is the midpoint of MN, if we can prove that $RQ \cdot RP = \overline{RM}^2$, the theorem will be proved. (Theorem 44, page 69.)

$$
\begin{aligned}
RQ \cdot RP &= (RP - QP)RP \\
&= \overline{RP}^2 - QP \cdot RP \\
&= \overline{OP}^2 - \overline{OR}^2 - OP \cdot PP' \ (\triangle ORP \text{ is rt. angled: } O, \\
&\qquad P', Q, R, \text{ are concyclic)} \\
&= \overline{OP}^2 - (\overline{OM}^2 - \overline{RM}^2) - OP \cdot PP' \ (\triangle OMR \text{ is rt.} \\
&\qquad \text{angled)} \\
&= \overline{OP}^2 - \overline{OA}^2 + \overline{RM}^2 - OP \cdot PP' \\
&= \overline{OP}^2 - \overline{OA}^2 + \overline{RM}^2 - OP(OP - OP') \\
&= \overline{OP}^2 - \overline{OA}^2 + \overline{RM}^2 - \overline{OP}^2 + OP \cdot OP' \\
&= \overline{RM}^2 \qquad (\overline{OA}^2 = OP \cdot OP').
\end{aligned}
$$

This proves the theorem.

Historical Note.   Desargues employed the ideas of pole and polar but not the terms.   The terms pole and polar came into use about the beginning of the nineteenth century.

THEOREM 63.   *If through a fixed point P a variable secant is drawn to cut a circle in M and N, the locus of the harmonic conjugate of P with respect to M and N is the polar of P with respect to the circle.*

This follows from Theorem 62, page 87.

THEOREM 64.   *If the polar of a point P passes through a point Q, the polar of Q passes through P.*

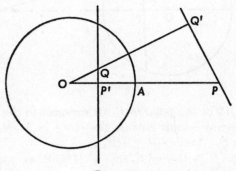

Figure 77

Proof: Let QP' be the polar of P.

Let OQ and the perpendicular on it from P intersect at Q'.

$OQ \cdot OQ' = OP' \cdot OP$ (Theorem 4, page 19)(Q, P', P, Q' are concyclic)

$$= \overline{OA}^2.$$

Hence $Q'P$ is the polar of Q.

This proves the theorem.

COROLLARY 1.   *The point of intersection of two lines is the pole of the line joining the poles of the given lines.*

COROLLARY 2.   *The line joining two points is the polar of the point of intersection of the polars of these points.*

COROLLARY 3.   *The polars of all points on a line are concurrent.*

Definitions.   If the polar of each of two points with respect to a circle passes through the other point the two points are called *conjugate points* with respect to the circle.

If the pole of each of two lines with respect to a circle lies on the other line the two lines are called *conjugate lines* with respect to the circle.

The triangle formed by the polars of the vertices of a given triangle with respect to a circle, is called the *conjugate* triangle of the given triangle.

A triangle each vertex of which is the pole of the opposite side with respect to a circle is called a *self-conjugate triangle*, and the circle is called the *polar circle* of the triangle.

EXERCISES

1. P and Q are conjugate points. If P is fixed, what is the locus of Q?
2. p and q are conjugate lines. If p is fixed, what is the locus of q?
3. Prove that if triangle $A'B'C'$ is the conjugate of triangle ABC, then ABC is the conjugate of $A'B'C'$.
4. Construct a triangle that is self-conjugate with respect to a given circle.
5. Where is the center of the polar circle of a given triangle?
6. Prove that a triangle has only one polar circle.
7. What is the polar circle of a right triangle?
8. An acute triangle has no polar circle.
9. The pole of a line joining two conjugate points with respect to a circle is the orthocenter of the triangle whose vertices are the two points and the center of the circle.
10. If a variable chord of a circle passes through a fixed point, the tangents at its extremeties intersect on a fixed line.
11. What are the poles of the sides of a triangle with respect to (a) its inscribed circle? (b) its circumscribed circle?
12. The polars of the vertices of a square with respect to its circumscribed circle enclose a square.
13. By employing the line at infinity, show that the polar of the center of a circle is the line at infinity, and that the pole of a diameter is the point at infinity in the direction perpendicular to that diameter.
14. Show that perpendicular diameters of a circle are conjugate lines with respect to the circle.
15. Show that the nine-point circle of a triangle is the inverse of the circumcircle with respect to the polar circle of the triangle.

THEOREM 65. (*Brianchon's Theorem.*) *If a hexagon is circumscribed about a circle, the diagonals joining opposite vertices are concurrent.*

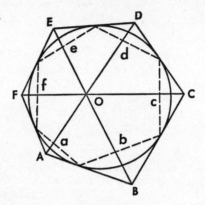

Figure 78

Proof: Let *ABCDEF* be a hexagon circumscribed about the circle.

The polars of the vertices *A*, *B*, *C*, *D*, *E*, *F*, form the sides of the inscribed polygon whose sides are *a*, *b*, *c*, *d*, *e*, *f*.

Since *a* is the polar of *A* and *d* is the polar of *D*, then the point of intersection of *a* and *d*, call it *L*, is the pole of *AD*.   (Theorem 64, Cor. 1, page 88.)

Likewise the point of intersection of *b* and *e*, call it *M*, is the pole of *BE*; and the point of intersection of *c* and *f*, call it *N*, is the pole of *CF*.

Now by Pascal's Theorem, page 60, *L*, *M*, *N* are collinear. Hence, their polars *AD*, *BE*, *CF* are concurrent.   (Theorem 64, Cor. 3, page 88.)

This proves the theorem.

Historical Note.   Brianchon's Theorem was published in a memoir in 1806.   It was the first example of such a use of the idea of poles and polars, and one of the earliest uses of the principle of duality. Pascal's and Brianchon's theorems are fundamental in the projective theory of conics.

Exercise. Assume Brianchon's Theorem and by using the relation of pole and polar prove that Pascal's Theorem follows.

EXERCISES

1. If a triangle be circumscribed about a circle, the lines joining the vertices to the points of tangency of the opposite sides are concurrent. Show that it is a special case of Brianchon's Theorem.
2. If a point moves along a straight line, its polar turns around a fixed point, and conversely.
3. What is the locus of the poles of a family of parallel lines?
4. If a secant through a point P cuts a circle in M, N, and the polar of P in Q, then $O\{PQ, MN\} = -1$, where O is the center of the circle.
5. Two tangents are drawn to a circle from a point Q on the polar of a point P. The two tangents, the polar, and the line PQ form a harmonic pencil.
6. The acute angle formed by two intersecting lines, equals the angle formed by the lines joining their poles to the center of the circle.
7. Two tangents from a point P touch a circle at R and S. A tangent at another point P' on the circle meets the secant RS at Q. Prove (1) that PP' is the polar of Q; (2) that $P\{RS, P'Q\} = -1$.
8. The center of a circle with respect to which a triangle is self-conjugate is at the orthocenter of the triangle, and its radius is a mean proportional between HA and HD, where H is the orthocenter and D is the foot of the altitude from A.
9. If four points form a harmonic range, their polars form a harmonic pencil, and conversely.

CHAPTER 9 Orthogonal Circles

Definitions. *The angle between two intersecting curves* is defined to be the angle between the tangents to the curves at the point of intersection.

If two curves intersect at right angles they are said to be *orthogonal*.

THEOREM 66. *The angle between two intersecting circles at one point of intersection equals the angle between them at the other.*

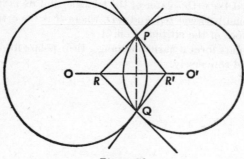

Figure 79

Proof: Let the two circles with centers O and O' intersect at P and Q. Let the tangents at P intersect the tangents at Q in R and R'.

The line of centers OO' passes through R and R'. For OO' is the perpendicular bisector of PQ and $RP = RQ$; (Theorem 9 (2), page 30.)

The triangles PRR' and QRR' are congruent.

Hence, $\angle RPR' = \angle RQR'$.

This proves the theorem.

THEOREM 67. *Tangents from the points of intersection of orthogonal circles pass through their centers.*

This proof is left for the student.

THEOREM 68. *If the tangents at the point of intersection of two circles pass through the centers, the circles are orthogonal.*

The proof is left for the student.

THEOREM 69. *The sum of the squares of the radii of two orthogonal circles equals the square of the distance between their centers.*

The proof is left for the student.

THEOREM 70. *If the square of the distance between the centers of two circles is equal to the sum of the squares of the radii, the circles are orthogonal.*   (Theorem 106, page 127.)

EXERCISES

1. Show that the following condition for the orthogonality of two circles is thus established by Theorems 69 and 70. Two circles with radii of r_1 and r_2 and distance d between their centers are orthogonal if and only if $r_1^2 + r_2^2 = d^2$.
2. What is the locus of the intersections of two variable orthogonal circles having fixed centers? Draw several pairs of the circles and construct the locus.
3. Prove that the sum of the areas of any two orthogonal circles having fixed centers is a constant.
4. The quadrilateral whose vertices are the centers and points of inter-section of two orthogonal circles is cyclic.
5. Is it possible for the center of one of two orthogonal circles to lie on the other circle?
6. Is it possible for the center of one of two orthogonal circles to lie within the other?

THEOREM 71. *If two circles are orthogonal, a diameter of one is cut harmonically by the other.*

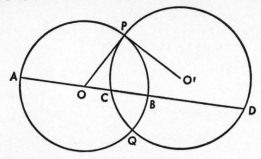

Figure 80

Proof: Suppose the circles with centers O and O' are orthogonal. Let the diameter AB passing through O cut the other circle in C and D.

$$OC \cdot OD = \overline{OP}^2 = \overline{OB}^2.   \text{(OP is a tangent.)}$$

Then $\{AB, CD\} = -1.$ (Theorem 44, page 69.)

COROLLARY. *Two circles are orthogonal if one passes through a pair of points that are inverse with respect to the other.*

EXERCISES

1. If two circles are orthogonal, every diameter of the first that cuts the second cuts it in points that are inverse with respect to the first.
2. Construct a circle orthogonal to a given circle and passing through two given points, (a) when the given points do not lie on the given circle; (b) when they lie on the given circle; (c) when they are collinear with the center of the given circle.
3. Construct a circle with a given center and orthogonal to a given circle. Is there more than one solution? Discuss the possibilities when the given center is without, on, and within the given circle.
4. Discuss the construction in Exercise 3 if the given circle is a straight line.
5. If two points divide a diameter of a circle harmonically, any circle through the two points is orthogonal to the given circle.

6. A common tangent to two circles touches them at A and B. Prove that a circle with diameter AB is orthogonal to the two circles.

7. If the sum of the angles in the segments of two intersecting circles on opposite sides of the common chord equals 90° the circles are orthogonal.

8. If two circles are orthogonal, the center of each is without the other.

9. The circle with respect to which a triangle is self-conjugate is orthogonal to the circles described on the sides of the triangle as diameters.

10. If H is the orthocenter of the triangle ABC, the circles described on AB and CH as diameters are orthogonal.

11. Construct a circle orthogonal to two given circles and having a given radius.

12. Through a given point to draw a circle of given radius to cut a given circle orthogonally.

13. Through a given point to draw a circle which cuts two given circles orthogonally.

14. If two circles are orthogonal, the extremities of any diameter of either are conjugate points with respect to the points of intersection of the diameter with the other circle.

CHAPTER 10 Radical Axis —
Coaxal Circles

Definitions. If O is the center of a circle of radius r and P is any point, then $\overline{OP}^2 - r^2$ is called the *power of the point* with respect to the circle.

COROLLARY 1. *The power of an external point with respect to a circle is the square of the tangent from the point to the circle.*

COROLLARY 2. *The power of an external point is positive and the power of an internal point is negative.*

Definition. The locus of a point, whose powers with respect to two circles are equal is called the *radical axis* of the circles.

EXERCISES

1. What is the power of (a) the center of a circle with respect to the circle? (b) a point on the circle?
2. Where is a point located with reference to a circle if its power with respect to that circle is (a) r^2? (b) $3r^2$? (c) $r^2/8$? (d) 0?
3. Prove that the power of a point within a circle is negative and equal numerically to the square of half the shortest chord passing through the given point.
4. Prove that if two circles are tangent internally or externally their common tangent at their point of contact is their radical axis.
5. The locus of a point having a given power with respect to a given circle is a circle concentric with the given circle.

THEOREM 72. *The radical axis of two circles is a straight line perpendicular to their line of centers.*

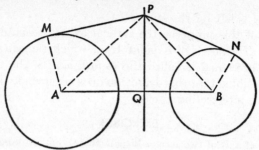

Figure 81

Proof: Let P be a point on the radical axis of two circles whose centers are A and B. Draw PM and PN tangents to the circles, and $PQ \perp AB$.

$$\overline{PA}^2 - \overline{AM}^2 = \overline{PB}^2 - \overline{BN}^2 \quad \text{(Definition of radical axis)}$$

Then $\overline{AQ}^2 + \overline{PQ}^2 - \overline{AM}^2 = \overline{QB}^2 + \overline{PQ}^2 - \overline{BN}^2$, ($\triangle PQA$ and $\triangle PQB$ are right $\triangle$s).

$$\overline{AQ}^2 - \overline{AM}^2 = \overline{QB}^2 - \overline{BN}^2,$$

and $$\overline{AQ}^2 - \overline{QB}^2 = \overline{AM}^2 - \overline{BN}^2.$$

Therefore $(AQ + QB)(AQ - QB) = \overline{AM}^2 - \overline{BN}^2$

and $$AQ - QB = \frac{\overline{AM}^2 - \overline{BN}^2}{AQ + QB} = \text{a constant.}$$

Hence the position of Q is independent of the position of P.

Therefore P always lies in the line $\perp AB$ at Q. This proves the theorem.

The proof is similar when the two circles intersect, and when one circle lies within the other.

EXERCISES

1. Prove Theorem 72 when the two circles intersect.
2. Prove Theorem 72 when one circle lies within the other.

THEOREM 73.　*Tangents to two circles from any point on their radical axis are equal.*

The proof is left for the student.

Because of this property the radical axis is sometimes defined as follows: The locus of a point from which tangents drawn to two circles are equal is called the *radical axis* of the two circles. It should be noted that this definition does not include the common chord of two intersecting circles.

EXERCISES

1. The radical axis of two circles bisects their common tangents.
2. For each of the following pairs of circles find the distance from the center of each circle to the radical axis. Let r_1 and r_2 denote the radii and d the distance between the centers.

	r_1	r_2	d			r_1	r_2	d
(a)	6	4	12		(g)	6	4	0
(b)	6	4	10		(h)	6	0	8
(c)	6	4	8		(i)	6	0	6
(d)	6	4	2		(j)	6	0	4
(e)	6	4	1		(k)	6	0	0
(f)	6	4	0.1		(l)	0	0	6

Sketch each figure. Tell the position of the radical axis with reference to the two circles in each case.

3. What is the position of the radical axis of (a) Two intersecting circles? (b) Two tangent circles? (c) Two circles, one within the other? (d) Two concentric circles? (e) A circle and a point circle? (f) Two point circles? (g) A point circle and a straight line?

4. If from a point P on the radical axis of two circles lines are drawn cutting one circle in A and B and the other in C and D, then $PA \cdot PB = PC \cdot PD$.

5. Prove that the four points A, B, C, D, in Exercise 4 are concyclic.

6. Prove the following construction for the radical axis of two circles. Draw a third circle cutting one given circle in A and B and the other in C and D. Draw lines AB and CD intersecting in P. Draw a second circle cutting one of the given circles in M and N and the other in R and S. Draw lines MN and RS intersecting in Q. Then PQ is the radical axis of the given circles.

THEOREM 74.   *The three radical axes of three circles taken in pairs are concurrent.*

Let the student give the proof.

Definition.   The point of concurrence of the three radical axes of three circles taken in pairs is called the *radical center* of the three circles.

EXERCISES

1. When two inverse circles intersect, the circle through their common points and the center of inversion inverts into their radical axis.
2. The locus of a point, the difference of whose powers with respect to two given circles is constant, is a straight line parallel to the radical axes of the circles.
3. If two circles intersect in A and B, the powers of any point on the line AB with respect to the two circles are equal.
4. What is the locus of a point whose powers with respect to two given circles are equal?
5. The radical axis of two circles is equally distant from the two polars of either center of similitude.
6. A circle with its center P on the radical axis of two given circles, and its radius the tangent from P to one of the given circles is orthogonal to the given circles.
7. What is the locus of the centers of circles orthogonal to two given circles?
8. A circle C intersects each of two circles C_1 and C_2.   Prove that the common chords of C and C_1 and C and C_2 meet on the radical axis of C_1 and C_2.
9. A circle with center at O on the radical axis of two circles has a radius equal to the tangent from O to one of the circles.   Prove that it is orthogonal to each of the two circles.
10. If $\{AB, CD\}$ is harmonic, the circle on AB as diameter is orthogonal to any circle through C and D.
11. Given two circles and their four common tangents.   Prove that the midpoints of the segments of the tangents between their points of contact are collinear.
12. The polar of either limiting point of a coaxal system with regard to any circle of the system passes through the other limiting point.

THEOREM 75. *If a system of circles be drawn having their centers on a fixed diameter (produced) of a given circle and orthogonal to it, the radical axis of any pair of circles of the system is a straight line passing through the center of the given circle and perpendicular to the fixed diameter.*

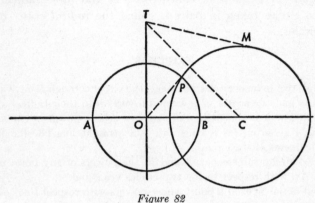

Figure 82

Proof: Given a circle with center O, with a fixed diameter AB.

Let C, a point on AB extended, be the center of a circle orthogonal to the given circle, P a point of intersection of the two circles, and T any point on a $\perp$ to OB at O. TM is a tangent to the circle with center C.

Then
$$\overline{TM}^2 = \overline{CT}^2 - \overline{CP}^2$$
$$= \overline{OT}^2 + \overline{OC}^2 - \overline{CP}^2$$
$$= \overline{OT}^2 + \overline{OP}^2 = \overline{TB}^2$$
$$= \text{a constant.}$$

Hence the length of TM is independent of the position of C.

Therefore OT is the radical axis of every pair of circles of the system.

Definitions. A system of circles any pair of which has the same radical axis as any other pair is called a *coaxal system.*

Since $\overline{OC}^2 - \overline{CP}^2 = \overline{OP}^2 = \overline{OB}^2$, OC is not less than OB. Hence C does not lie within the given circle. As C approaches B, CP

approaches zero, and B is called a *limiting point* of the system of coaxal circles. A is also a limiting point. The limiting points are point circles of the system.

THEOREM 76. *A system of circles passing through two points and having their centers on the perpendicular bisector of the line joining the points form a coaxal system.*

The proof is left for the student.

PROBLEM 7. *To construct the radical axes of each pair of a system of three circles.*

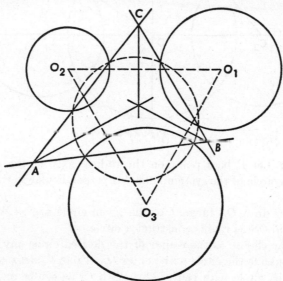

Figure 83

Solution: Given the three circles with centers O_1, O_2, O_3.

Draw any fourth circle cutting each of the three circles and draw the three radical axes of the fourth circle and each of the three given circles. Let these radical axes intersect in A, B, C.

Draw a $\perp$ from A to O_2O_3, from B to O_3O_1, from C to O_1O_2. Prove that these three perpendiculars are the three desired radical axes.

PROBLEM 8.   *To construct a coaxal system of circles given one circle of the system and the radical axis which does not meet the given circle.*

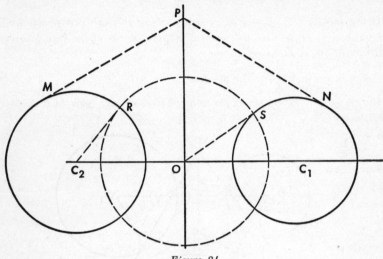

Figure 84

Solution: Let P be a point on the radical axis, C_1 the center of the given circle of the system, and C_1O perpendicular to the radical axis.

From O draw OS tangent to the given circle at S. With O as center and OS as radius construct a circle.

We now choose as the center of the desired circle any point C_2 on C_1O outside the circle with center O. From C_2 draw a tangent C_2R to the circle with center O. With C_2 as center and C_2R as radius draw a circle. This circle is coaxal with the given circle.

Proof:
$$\overline{PM}^2 = \overline{PC_2}^2 - \overline{C_2M}^2$$
$$= \overline{PO}^2 + \overline{OC_2}^2 - \overline{C_2M}^2$$
$$= \overline{PO}^2 + \overline{OR}^2 + \overline{C_2R}^2 - \overline{C_2M}^2$$
$$= \overline{PO}^2 + \overline{OR}^2.$$

Similarly, $\overline{PN}^2 = \overline{PO}^2 + \overline{OS}^2.$

Therefore, $\overline{PM}^2 = \overline{PN}^2$,

and OP is the radical axis of the two circles.

It is apparent that a circle of the system may be drawn using for its center any point on C_1O outside of the circle with center O.

PROBLEM 9. *To construct a system of coaxal circles given one circle of the system and the radical axis which cuts the circle.*

The construction is left for the student.

PROBLEM 10. *To construct a system of coaxal circles given one circle of the system and the radical axis which is tangent to the given circle.*

The construction is left for the student.

THEOREM 77. *For every system of coaxal circles there exists a second system of coaxal circles such that every circle of each system cuts every circle of the other system orthogonally.*

Proof: Tangents drawn from any point on the radical axis of the given system to the circles of the system are equal. Hence a circle drawn with a radius equal to such a tangent and with its center at P on the radical axis is orthogonal to every circle of the given system. Hence there exists a second system of circles with centers on the radical axis of the given system orthogonal to the given coaxal system.

This second system is a coaxal system. For from the center of any circle C of the given coaxal system tangents to the circles of the second system are all radii of C and hence equal, since C is orthogonal to every circle of the second system. Hence the circles of the second set are coaxal and their radical axis is the line of centers of the circles of the given coaxal system.

EXERCISES

1. AB is a common tangent of two non-intersecting circles. Prove that the circle on AB as a diameter passes through the limiting points of the system of coaxal circles of which the two circles are members.

2. The tangents drawn to every circle of a coaxal system from a limiting point are bisected by the radical axis.

3. A straight line is the radical axis of its inverse and the circle of inversion.

4. The circles of a coaxal system are tangent at a point P. Prove that the limiting points of the system coincide at P.

5. The polars of a fixed point with respect to the circles of a coaxal system are concurrent.

6. If two systems of coaxal circles have one circle in common, they have a common orthogonal circle.

7. The inverse of a system of concurrent lines is a system of coaxal circles.

8. Show that the circle of inversion may be chosen so that the inverses of three given circles will be coincident with themselves.

CHAPTER 11

Cross Ratio

Definition. If A, B, C, D be a range of four points, then $\dfrac{AC}{CB} : \dfrac{AD}{DB}$ is called a *cross ratio*, or *anharmonic ratio*, of the range, and is indicated by $\{AB, CD\}$.

The direction of the segments is taken into account.

Since four letters permit of 24 permutations, there are 24 ways in which a cross ratio of four points may be written. These cross ratios are not however all different in value.

THEOREM 78. *The cross ratio of four points is unchanged in value when two of the points are interchanged if also the other points are interchanged; that is,*

$$\{AB, CD\} = \{BA, DC\} = \{CD, AB\} = \{DC, BA\}.$$

Proof:
$$\{AB, CD\} = \frac{AC}{CB} : \frac{AD}{DB} = \frac{AC \cdot DB}{CB \cdot AD} \cdot$$

$$\{BA, DC\} = \frac{BD}{DA} : \frac{BC}{CA} = \frac{AC \cdot DB}{CB \cdot AD} \cdot$$

$$\{CD, AB\} = \frac{CA}{AD} : \frac{CB}{BD} = \frac{AC \cdot DB}{CB \cdot AD} \cdot$$

$$\{DC, BA\} = \frac{DB}{BC} : \frac{DA}{AC} = \frac{AC \cdot DB}{CB \cdot AD} \cdot$$

This proves the theorem.

EXERCISES

1. Compute: $\{AB, CD\}$, $\{BA, DC\}$, $\{BA, CD\}$, and $\{CA, BD\}$, for Figure 85.

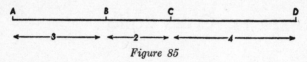

Figure 85

2. Verify Theorem 78 for the ranges A, B, C, D, if
   (a) $AB = 6$, $BC = 3$, $CD = 10$.   (b) $AC = 6$, $CB = 3$, $BD = 9$.

THEOREM 79. *If two points of one pair of a given cross ratio are interchanged but the other two are unchanged, the value of the resulting cross ratio is the reciprocal of the given one; that is, if $\{AB, CD\} = r$, then*

$$\{BA, CD\} = \{CD, BA\} = \{AB, DC\} = \{DC, AB\} = \frac{1}{r}.$$

Proof: $\{BA, CD\} = \dfrac{BC}{CA} : \dfrac{BD}{DA} = \dfrac{CB \cdot AD}{AC \cdot DB} = \dfrac{1}{r}.$

The proof is at once completed by applying Theorem 78 to prove that each of the remaining three cross ratios equals the first.

COROLLARY. *If the value of $\{AB, CD\}$ is unchanged by interchanging two points of one pair the other two remaining unchanged, then $\{AB, CD\} = -1$.*

THEOREM 80. *If $\{AB, CD\} = r$, then*

$$\{AC, BD\} = \{BD, AC\} = \{CA, DB\} = \{DB, CA\} = 1 - r.$$

Proof: $\{AC, BD\} = \dfrac{AB}{BC} : \dfrac{AD}{DC} = \dfrac{AB \cdot DC}{BC \cdot AD}$

$$= \frac{(AC + CB)(DB + BC)}{BC \cdot AD}$$

$$= \frac{AC \cdot DB + AC \cdot BC + CB \cdot DB + CB \cdot BC}{BC \cdot AD}$$

$$= \frac{AC \cdot DB}{BC \cdot AD} + \frac{BC(AC - DB + CB)}{BC \cdot AD}$$

$$= - \frac{AC \cdot DB}{CB \cdot AD} + \frac{BC(AC + CB + BD)}{BC \cdot AD}$$

$$= -r + \frac{BC \cdot AD}{BC \cdot AD} = 1 - r.$$

Apply Theorem 78, page 105, to complete the proof.

COROLLARY 1. *If* $\{AB, CD\} = r$, *then*

$$\{BC, AD\} = \{AD, BC\} = \{CB, DA\} = \{DA, CB\} = \frac{r-1}{r}.$$

Proof: By Theorem 79, page 106, $\{BA, CD\} = \frac{1}{r}$,

and by Theorem 80, $\{BC, AD\} = 1 - \frac{1}{r} = \frac{r-1}{r}$.

COROLLARY 2. *If* $\{AB, CD\} = r$, *then*

$$\{CA, BD\} = \{AC, DB\} = \{BD, CA\} = \{DB, AC\} = \frac{1}{1 - r},$$

and $\{CB, AD\} = \{AD, CB\} = \{BC, DA\} = \{DA, BC\} = \frac{r}{r-1}$.

Hint. Apply Theorem 79, page 106.

In Theorems 78, 79, 80 and their corollaries we have examined the 24 cross ratios of four points.   Hence we have now proved that the 24 possible cross ratios of four points may be arranged into six groups of four each, all of the ratios in each group having the same value.   It appears also that 12 of these cross ratios are the reciprocals of the other 12.

In discussions involving cross ratio it is customary to use the same cross ratio throughout and the numerical value is seldom important.   It is not then necessary to state which of the cross ratios of a given range is used.

EXERCISES

1. If the range $ABCD$ be inverted with respect to a point on the same line into $A'B'C'D'$, then $\{AB, CD\} = \{A'B', C'D'\}$.
2. If $\{AB, CD\} = -1$, show that the six possible values of the cross ratio are $-1, 2, 1/2$.

3. If a pencil of four lines is cut in ranges $ABCD$ and $A'B'C'D'$ by two parallel lines, then $\{AB, CD\} = \{A'B', C'D'\}$.

4. Verify Corollaries 1 and 2, page 107 when $AB = 4$, $AC = -3$, $CD = -6$.

5. Verify Theorem 79, page 106, for the ranges A, B, C, D, if
   (a) $AC = 10$, $CD = 4$, $DB = 8$.
   (b) $AC = 6$, $CB = 2$, $BD = 4$.

6. Verify Theorem 80, page 106, for the ranges A, B, C, D if
   (a) $AC = 2$, $CB = 8$, $AD = -1/3$.
   (b) $AC = -2$, $AB = 2$, $BD = 2$.

Definition. A *cross ratio of the pencil of lines* OA, OB, OC, OD, is defined to be

$$\frac{\sin AOC}{\sin COB} : \frac{\sin AOD}{\sin DOB},$$

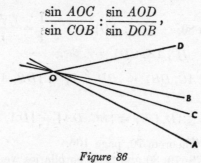

Figure 86

and is denoted by the symbol $O\{AB, CD\}$.

In this definition the sign of the angle is taken into account.

THEOREM 81. *The cross ratio of a pencil of four lines is equal to the cross ratio of the range cut from the pencil by any transversal.*

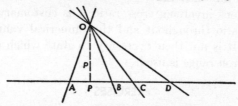

Figure 87

To prove that $\dfrac{AC}{CB} : \dfrac{AD}{DB} = \dfrac{\sin AOC}{\sin COB} : \dfrac{\sin AOD}{\sin DOB}.$

The signs of the two cross ratios are the same. This may be seen by noting the sign of each of the four ratios.

Proof: $\triangle AOC = \frac{1}{2}p \cdot AC$, $\triangle COB = \frac{1}{2}p \cdot CB$,

$\triangle AOD = \frac{1}{2}p \cdot AD$, $\triangle DOB = \frac{1}{2}p \cdot DB$.

$$\therefore \frac{\triangle AOC}{\triangle COB} : \frac{\triangle AOD}{\triangle DOB} = \frac{AC}{CB} : \frac{AD}{DB}.$$

$$\triangle AOC = \frac{1}{2}AO \cdot CO \cdot \sin \angle AOC,$$

$$\triangle COB = \frac{1}{2}CO \cdot BO \cdot \sin \angle COB,$$

$$\triangle AOD = \frac{1}{2}AO \cdot DO \cdot \sin \angle AOD,$$

$$\triangle DOB = \frac{1}{2}DO \cdot OB \cdot \sin \angle DOB.$$

$$\therefore \frac{\triangle AOC}{\triangle COB} : \frac{\triangle AOD}{\triangle DOB} = \frac{\sin \angle AOC}{\sin \angle COB} \cdot \frac{\sin \angle AOD}{\sin \angle DOB}.$$

$$\therefore \frac{AC}{CB} : \frac{AD}{DB} = \frac{\sin \angle AOC}{\sin \angle COB} : \frac{\sin \angle AOD}{\sin \angle DOB},$$

or $\{AB, CD\} = O\{AB, CD\}.$

Definition. Ranges or pencils, with equal cross ratios are called *equicross*.

THEOREM 82. *Ranges cut from a pencil of four lines by any two transversals are equicross.*

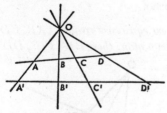

Figure 88

Proof: $\{AB, CD\} = O\{AB, CD\} = \{A'B', C'D'\}.$

Theorem 82 proves that the cross ratio of a range of four points is unchanged by a projection. This is a basic theorem of projective geometry.

THEOREM 83.   *Two pencils subtended by the same range are equicross.*

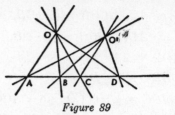

Figure 89

Let the student prove that

$$O\{AB, CD\} = O'\{AB, CD\}.$$

THEOREM 84.   *If $\{AB, CD\}$ and $\{A'B', C'D'\}$ are any two equicross ranges, and if AA', BB', CC' are concurrent, then DD' passes through the point of concurrence.*

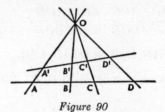

Figure 90

The proof is the same as that of Theorem 49, page 72.   Let the student make the proof.

THEOREM 85.   *If two equicross ranges $\{AB, CD\}$ and $\{AB', C'D'\}$ have the point A in common, then BB', CC', DD' are concurrent.*

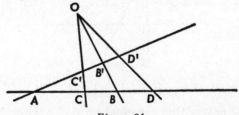

Figure 91

Show that this is a particular case of Theorem 84.

THEOREM 86. *If pencils O{AB, CD} and O'{AB, CD} are equicross, and if A, B, C are collinear, then D lies on the line ABC.*

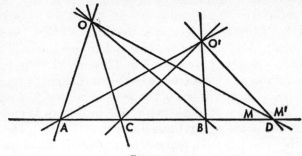

Figure 92

The proof is the same as that of Theorem 51, page 74.

THEOREM 87. *If pencils O{AB, CD} and O'{AB, CD} are equicross, and if O' lies on OD, then A, B, C are collinear.*

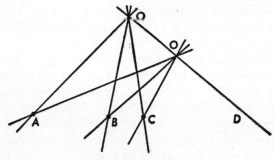

Figure 93

Show that this is a particular case of Theorem 86.

Projective Geometry. In Euclidian geometry it is assumed that a figure may be moved about in space without changing its size or shape. Such a motion of a figure is called a *rigid motion.* Lengths of lines and sizes of angles are *invariant,* that is, they are unchanged by such a motion. A property of a figure, such as length, that depends upon measuring, is called a *metric* property.

Euclidean geometry is almost entirely a *metric geometry* since it deals in general with metric properties of figures.

A property of a figure that is invariant of projection (see page 111) is called a *projective property*. In Figure 88, page 109, the range $A'B'C'D'$ is the projection of the range $ABCD$. As appears in this figure, lengths may be changed by projection. So also may angles. But we have proved in Theorem 82, page 109, that the cross ratio of a range of four points is not changed by projection.

Projective geometry is one of the most important movements of modern geometry. It deals with the projective properties of figures in the plane and in three-dimensional space. The invariance of the cross ratio of a range of four points is one of the fundamental theorems of projective geometry.

This invariance of the cross ratio may have been known to Euclid (300 B.C.) and to Menelaus (100 A.D.). It is mentioned by the Greek mathematical historian, Pappus (300 A.D.). But little was added to the ideas that were combined into the subject of projective geometry until Gerard Desargues (1593–1662) discovered the important theorem bearing his name, Theorem 41, page 62. This theorem is also true if the triangles lie in different planes.

The contributions to projective geometry were in the main isolated theorems until the work of Jean Victor Poncelet (1788–1867). He began his work while a prisoner of war in a Russian camp on the Volga River. Poncelet set himself the problem of studying the properties of geometric figures that do not involve the measurement either of lines or of angles. He developed the projective invariance of the harmonic range of four points but the invariance of the general cross ratio was unknown to him.

It is readily seen that the theory of projective geometry is the basis of the methods of descriptive geometry which has the problem of representing three-dimensional figures in a plane, an important problem for painters, architects, and builders.

This brief note on the history of projective geometry gives an example of the slow growth through centuries of an important scientific theory. The dependence of modern progress upon ancient thought is often illustrated in the history of mathematics.

CHAPTER 12

Principle of Duality

Duality. Many theorems of geometry involving points and lines remain true if the points are changed into lines and the lines are changed into points. This is an example of the *Principle of Duality*.

We shall denote points by capital letters, $A, B, C, \ldots$, and lines by small letters, $a, b, c, \ldots$. We shall denote the line connecting points A and B by AB, and the point of intersection of lines a and b by ab.

Examples.

2 points determine 1 line.

If a point lies on a fixed line its polar passes through a fixed point.

If $\{AB, CD\}$ and $\{AB', C'D'\}$ are equicross ranges on different lines, then the lines BB', CC', DD' are concurrent.

A point moving under certain conditions defines a curve, its locus.

2 lines determine 1 point.

If a line passes through a fixed point its pole lies on a fixed line.

If $\{ab, cd\}$ and $\{ab', c'd'\}$ are equicross pencils with different vertices, then the points of intersection bb', cc', dd' are collinear.

A line moving under certain conditions defines a curve, its envelope.

Point and line are called *dual elements*.

Drawing a line through a point and marking a point on a line are called *dual operations*.

If, in a figure whose elements are points and lines, each element is replaced by its dual element, and each operation by its dual

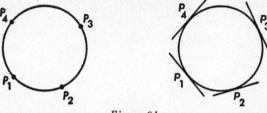

Figure 94

operation, the resulting figure is called the *dual figure* of the given one.

Examples of Dual Figures.

a. A range of three points A, B, and C on the line p form a dual figure of three lines a, b, c through the point P.

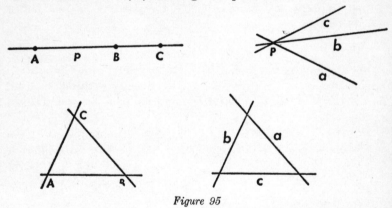

Figure 95

b. Three non-collinear points A, B, and C and the lines joining them form a dual figure of three non-concurrent lines a, b, and c and their points of intersection.

c. In three dimensions the point and the plane are dual elements. Thus in general three points determine a plane; and three planes determine a point. State the exception in each case.

Definition. If in a given theorem concerning points and lines, each element and each operation is replaced by its dual, the resulting theorem is called the *dual theorem* of the given one.

EXERCISES

1. Draw the dual figure of each of the following:

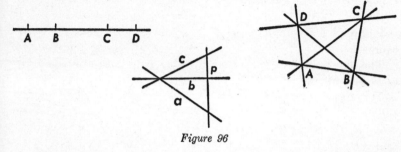

Figure 96

2. Given five points, no three collinear, and all the lines joining them. Construct the dual figure.

3. State the dual of each of the following theorems:
   (a) n points, no three of which are collinear, determine $\frac{1}{2}n(n-1)$ lines.
   (b) The line joining any two points A and B is the polar of the point of intersection of the polars of A and B.
   (c) Desargues Theorem.

4. The ranges cut from a pencil of four lines by two parallel lines are equicross.

5. If $\{AB, CD\} = \{AB, CD'\}$, then D and D' coincide.

6. Determine the conditions under which $\{AB, CD\} = 1$.

7. If four points are collinear, their polars with respect to a circle are concurrent, and the cross ratio of the pencil so formed is equal to the cross ratio of the range of four points.

8. Four fixed points on a circle subtend at a variable point on the circle a pencil of constant cross ratio.

9. If two triangles are inscribed in a circle, any two sides, one chosen from each triangle, cut equicross ranges from the other four sides.
   Hint. Apply the preceding exercise.

10. State and prove the converse of Desargues Theorem, page 62.

11. State the dual of Exercise 4.

12. State a theorem of elementary geometry and its dual theorem.

The Complete Quadrangle and the Complete Quadrilateral.

Complete Quadrangle

The figure formed by four points, no three collinear, and the six lines joining them is called a *complete quadrangle*.

Figure 97 is a complete quadrangle.

The four points are called the *vertices* and the six lines the *sides* of the complete quadrangle.

A, B, C, D are the vertices and *AB, AC, AD, BC, BD, CD* are the sides.

Complete Quadrilateral

The figure formed by four lines, no three concurrent, and the six points in which they intersect, is called a *complete quadrilateral*.

Figure 98 is a complete quadrilateral.

The four lines are called the *sides* and the six points the *vertices* of the complete quadrilateral.

a, b, c, d are the sides and *ab, ac, ad, bc, bd, cd* are the vertices.

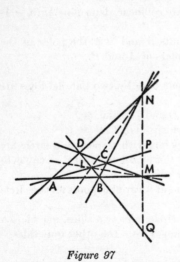

Figure 97

Complete Quadrangle

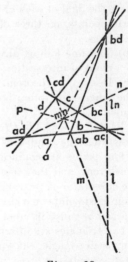

Figure 98

Complete Quadrilateral

Opposite sides are sides that do not pass through the same vertex. AB and CD, AD and BC, AC and DB are opposite sides.

Points of intersection of opposite sides are called *diagonal points*. L, M, N are diagonal points.

Opposite vertices are vertices that do not lie on the same side. ab and cd, ad and bc, ac and db are opposite vertices.

Lines joining opposite vertices are called *diagonals*. l, m, n are diagonals.

We shall now prove the theorem of the harmonic property of the complete quadrangle and of the complete quadrilateral.

Just as we have denoted the cross ratio of the pencil PA, PB, PC, PD by $P\{AB, CD\}$, we shall denote the cross ratio of the range pa, pb, pc, pd by $p\{ab, cd\}$.

THEOREM 88. *Through each diagonal point of a complete quadrangle there is a harmonic pencil composed of two sides of the quadrangle and the lines joining this diagonal point with the other two diagonal points.*

THEOREM 89. *On each diagonal of a complete quadrilateral there is a harmonic range composed of two vertices of the quadrilateral and the points of intersection of this diagonal with the other two diagonals.*

Proof: $\{AC, LP\} = N\{AC, LP\}$

$$= \{DB, LQ\}$$
$$= M\{DB, LQ\}$$
$$= \{CA, LP\}$$

$\{ac, lp\} = n\{ac, lp\}$

$$= \{db, lq\}$$
$$= m\{db, lq\}$$
$$= \{ca, lp\}$$

Hence $\{AC, LP\}$ is harmonic by Corollary, Theorem 79, page 106.

Hence $\{ac, lp\}$ is harmonic by Corollary, Theorem 79, page 106.

EXERCISE

1. In Figure 97, let NL and AB intersect at R. Prove $\{AB, RM\} = -1$.

   Hint. Consider $\triangle ABN$. Apply Ceva's Theorem, page 55, using lines AC, BD, and NR; also apply Menelaus' Theorem, page 57, using transversal DM.

THEOREM 90. *The midpoints of the diagonals of a complete quadrilateral are collinear.*

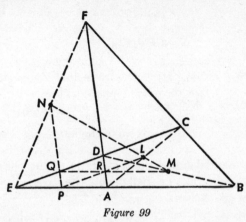

Figure 99

Let $ABCD$ be the complete quadrilateral with diagonals AC, BD, EF. Let L, M, N be the midpoints of the diagonals.

Consider the triangle ADE, the midpoints of whose sides are P, Q, R. PR is parallel to ED and passes through L; QR is parallel to AE and passes through M; and PQ is parallel to AD and passes through N. We may prove the theorem by proving that

$$\frac{LP}{LR} \cdot \frac{MQ}{MR} \cdot \frac{NP}{NQ} = 1.$$

Show that

$$\frac{LP}{LR} = \frac{CE}{CD}, \frac{MQ}{MR} = \frac{BE}{BA}, \frac{NP}{NQ} = \frac{FA}{FD},$$

and hence

$$\frac{LP}{LR} \cdot \frac{MQ}{MR} \cdot \frac{NP}{NQ} = \frac{CE}{CD} \cdot \frac{BE}{BA} \cdot \frac{FA}{FD} = 1$$

APPENDIX

The following material from elementary geometry is included in the text in order that references may be made to the numbered propositions. It is also available for review purposes. A few of these listed propositions are made an integral part of the text. The proofs of some propositions now usually omitted from elementary texts are also included here.

THEOREMS AND COROLLARIES
Rectilinear Figures

1. If two triangles have two sides and the included angle of one equal respectively to two sides and the included angle of the other, they are congruent.
2. If two triangles have two angles and the included side of one equal respectively to two angles and the included side of the other, they are congruent.
3. If two sides of a triangle are equal, the angles opposite these sides are equal.
4. If three sides of one triangle are equal respectively to three sides of another triangle, the two triangles are congruent.
5. Two points each equally distant from the ends of a line segment determine the perpendicular bisector of it.
6. An exterior angle of a triangle is greater than either of the opposite interior angles.
7. Only one perpendicular can be drawn to a line from an external point.
8. Two lines parallel to the same line are parallel to each other.
9. If two lines are cut by a transversal so that a pair of alternate interior angles are equal, the lines are parallel.
10. If two lines are cut by a transversal so that a pair of corresponding angles are equal, the lines are parallel.
11. If two lines are cut by a transversal so that a pair of interior angles on the same side of the transversal are supplementary, the lines are parallel.
12. Two lines in the same plane perpendicular to the same line are parallel.

13. If two parallel lines are cut by a transversal, the alternate interior angles are equal.

14. If two parallel lines are cut by a transversal, the corresponding angles are equal.

15. If two parallel lines are cut by a transversal, the interior angles on the same side of the transversal are supplementary.

16. A line perpendicular to one of two parallel lines is perpendicular to the other.

17. Two lines perpendicular to intersecting lines also intersect.

18. If two lines are cut by a transversal so that the two interior angles on the same side of the transversal are not supplementary the lines are not parallel.

19. If two angles have their sides parallel right side to right side and left side to left side, they are equal.

20. If two angles have their sides parallel right side to left side and left side to right side, they are supplementary.

21. The sum of the three angles of a triangle is a straight angle.

22. An exterior angle of a triangle is equal to the sum of the two opposite interior angles.

23. If two angles have their sides perpendicular right side to right side and left side to left side, they are equal.

24. If two angles have their sides perpendicular right side to left side, and left side to right side, they are supplementary.

25. The sum of the angles of a polygon of n sides is $(n-2)$ straight angles.

26. Each angle of a regular polygon of n sides is $\dfrac{n-2}{n}$ straight angles.

27. If two angles and any side of one triangle are equal respectively to two angles and the corresponding side of another triangle, the triangles are congruent.

28. If two angles of a triangle are equal, the sides opposite these angles are equal.

29. If two right triangles have a hypotenuse and leg of one equal respectively to the hypotenuse and leg of the other, they are congruent.

30. In a thirty-sixty degree right triangle, the hypotenuse is double the shorter leg.

31. The opposite sides of a parallelogram are equal, and the opposite angles are equal.

32. Parallel lines included between parallel lines are equal.

33. Two parallel lines are everywhere equidistant.

34. The diagonals of a parallelogram bisect each other.
35. If the opposite sides of a quadrilateral are equal, it is a parallelogram.
36. If two sides of a quadrilateral are equal and parallel, it is a parallelogram.
37. If the diagonals of a quadrilateral bisect each other, it is a parallelogram.
38. If three or more parallels cut off equal segments on one transversal, they cut off equal segments on every transversal.
39. If a line bisects one side of a triangle and is parallel to a second side, it bisects the third side.
40. A line joining the midpoints of two sides of a triangle is parallel to the third side and equal to one-half of it.
41. If two sides of a triangle are unequal, the angles opposite these sides are unequal, and the angle opposite the greater side is the greater.
42. Converse of 41.
43. The perpendicular is the shortest line that can be drawn from a point to a line and conversely.
44. If two sides of one triangle are equal respectively to two sides of another triangle, but the included angle of the first is greater than the included angle of the second, then the third side of the first is greater than the third side of the second.
45. Converse of 44.

Circles

46. In the same or equal circles, equal central angles have equal arcs.
47. In the same or equal circles, equal arcs have equal central angles.
48. In the same or equal circles, equal chords have equal arcs.
49. In the same or equal circles, equal arcs have equal chords.
50. A diameter perpendicular to a chord bisects the chord and its arcs.
51. The perpendicular bisector to a chord passes through the center of the circle.
52. A diameter which bisects a chord (that is not a diameter) is perpendicular to it.
53. Through three points not in a straight line one circle, and only one, can be drawn.
54. In the same circle or in equal circles, equal chords are equally distant from the center.
55. In the same circle or in equal circles, chords equally distant from the center are equal.
56. A tangent to a circle is perpendicular to the radius drawn to the point of contact.

57. A line perpendicular to the radius at its outer extremity is tangent to the circle.
58. Tangents to a circle from an external point are equal.
59. The number of degrees in a central angle is equal to the number of degrees in its arc, or a central angle is measured by its arc.
60. An angle inscribed in a circle is measured by half its intercepted arc.
61. An angle inscribed in a segment is greater than, equal to, or less than, a right angle, according as the segment is less than, equal to, or greater than a semicircle.
62. An angle formed by a tangent and a chord is measured by half its intercepted arc.
63. An angle formed by two chords intersecting within a circle is measured by one-half the sum of the intercepted arcs.
64. An angle formed (1) by two secants, (2) by a secant and a tangent, (3) by two tangents intersecting, in each case, outside a circle is measured by one-half the difference of the intercepted arcs.
65. The arcs of a circle intercepted between two parallel lines are equal.
66. In the same circle or in equal circles, if two central angles are unequal, the greater angle has the greater arc, and conversely.
67. If in the same circle or in equal circles, two minor arcs are unequal, the greater arc has the greater chord and conversely.
68. If in the same circle or in equal circles two chords are unequal, the greater chord is nearer the center and conversely.

Ratio and Proportion

69. A line parallel to one side of a triangle and intersecting the other two sides produced if necessary divides them proportionally.
70. If a line divides two sides of a triangle proportionally, it is parallel to the third side.
71. Corresponding segments cut off on two transversals by a series of parallels are proportional.
72. Two triangles are similar if three angles of one are equal respectively to the three angles of the other.
73. Two triangles are similar if two angles of one are equal respectively to two angles of the other.
74. Two triangles are similar if an angle of one equals an angle of the other and the including sides are proportional.
75. Triangles are similar if their corresponding sides are proportional.
76. Two similar polygons can be divided into triangles which are similar and similarly placed, and conversely.

77. If a perpendicular is drawn from the vertex of the right angle of a right triangle to the hypotenuse, (1) the two triangles thus formed are similar to the given triangle; (2) the perpendicular is the mean proportional between the segments of the hypotenuse; (3) each leg of the given triangle is the mean proportional between the hypotenuse and its adjacent segment.

78. The perpendicular to a diameter from any point on a circle is the mean proportional between the segments of the diameter.

79. If two chords intersect in a circle, the product of the parts of one is equal to the product of the parts of the other.

80. If from a point outside a circle a tangent and a secant are drawn to the circle, the tangent is the mean proportional between the whole secant and its external segment.

81. If from a point without a circle, two secants are drawn, the product of one secant and its external segment is equal to the product of the other secant and its external segment.

82. The square of the hypotenuse of a right triangle is equal to the sum of the squares of the other two sides.

Areas

83. The area of a rectangle is equal to the product of its base and its altitude.

84. The area of a parallelogram is equal to the product of its base and its altitude.

85. The area of a triangle is equal to one-half the product of its base and altitude.

86. If two triangles have the same altitude, their areas are to each other as their bases.

87. The area of a trapezoid is equal to one-half the product of its altitude and the sum of its bases.

88. The areas of two similar triangles have the same ratio as the squares of any two corresponding sides.

89. The areas of two similar polygons have the same ratio as the squares of any two corresponding sides.

90. The area of a regular polygon is equal to one-half the product of its apothem and its perimeter.

91. The area of a circle is equal to one-half the product of its radius by its circumference.   Or the area of a circle equals πr^2.

92. The areas of two circles are to each other as the squares of their radii, or as the squares of their diameters.

Regular Polygons and the Circle

93. An equilateral polygon inscribed in a circle is a regular polygon.
94. A circle can be circumscribed about any regular polygon.
95. A circle can be inscribed in any regular polygon.
96. If a circle is divided into equal arcs, the chords of these arcs form a regular inscribed polygon.
97. If a circle is divided into equal arcs, the tangents at the points of division form a regular circumscribed polygon.
98. Regular polygons of the same number of sides are similar.
99. The perimeters of two regular polygons of the same number of sides are to each other as their radii, or as their apothems.
100. The circumferences of two circles are to each other as their radii.
101. The circumference of a circle is equal to $2\pi r$.

PROBLEMS

1. To bisect a given line segment.
2. To construct a perpendicular to a line from a point outside the line.
3. To construct a perpendicular to a line at a point in the line.
4. To bisect a given angle.
5. To construct an angle equal to a given angle.
6. Through a given point to construct a line parallel to a given line.
7. To divide a line segment into any number of equal parts.
8. To construct a triangle when the three sides are given.
9. To construct a triangle given, two sides and the included angle.
10. To construct a triangle given, two angles and the included side.
11. To construct a triangle when two angles and the side opposite one of them are given.
12. To find the center of a circle when an arc is given.
13. To circumscribe a circle about a given triangle.
14. To inscribe a circle in a given triangle.
15. To construct a tangent to a circle at a point on the circle.
16. To construct a tangent to a circle from an external point.
17. To construct a fourth proportional to three given line segments.
18. To divide a line segment into parts proportional to two given line segments.
19. To construct the mean proportional between two given lines.
20. To construct a triangle similar to a given triangle.
21. To inscribe a square in a given circle.
22. To inscribe a regular hexagon in a given circle.

THEOREM 102. *The bisector of an interior angle of a triangle divides the opposite side internally into segments having the same ratio as the other two sides of the triangle.*

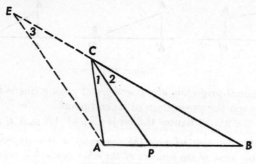

Figure 100

Given $\triangle ABC$, CP bisecting the angle C. Prove $AP/PB = AC/BC$.
Proof: Extend BC to intersect a parallel to CP through A.
$AP/PB = EC/CB$. Prove $CA = CE$ and substitute.

THEOREM 103. *The bisector of an exterior angle of a triangle divides the opposite side externally into segments having the same numerical ratio as the other two sides of the triangle.*

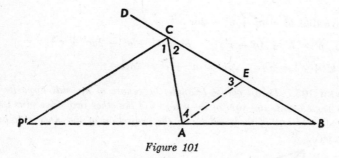

Figure 101

Proof: Draw $AE\|P'C$. $AP'/P'B = EC/CB$. Prove $AC = EC$ and substitute.

When a line is divided internally and externally into parts having the same numerical ratio, it is said to be divided *harmonically*. The line AB in the two propositions above has been divided harmonically by P and P', that is, $AP/PB = AP'/P'B$, not regarding signs.

Definition: The orthogonal *projection of a point upon a line* is the foot of the perpendicular from the point to the line.

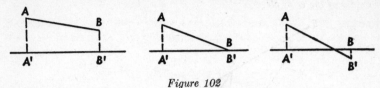

Figure 102

The orthogonal *projection of a line segment upon a line* is the segment included between the projections of its end points.

In each of the above figures the projection of AB is $A'B'$.

THEOREM 104. *In any triangle the square of a side opposite an acute angle equals the sum of the squares of the other two sides, minus twice the product of either side and the projection of the other side upon it.*

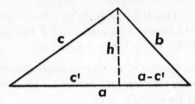

Figure 103

Prove that $b^2 = a^2 + c^2 - 2ac'$.

Proof: $b^2 = h^2 + (a - c')^2$ $b^2 = h^2 + a^2 - 2ac' + c'^2$

But $h^2 + c'^2 = c^2$ $\therefore b^2 = a^2 + c^2 - 2ac'$.

THEOREM 105. *In an obtuse triangle the square of the side opposite the obtuse angle equals the sum of the squares of the other two sides plus twice the product of one of these sides and the projection of the other side on it (extended).*

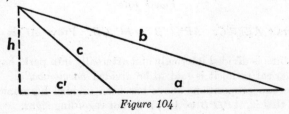

Figure 104

Prove that $b^2 = a^2 + c^2 + 2ac'$

Proof: (Left for the student).

THEOREM 106. *If in any triangle the square on one side equals the sum of the squares of the other two sides, the angle opposite the first side is a right angle.*

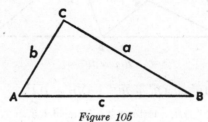

Figure 105

Given: $c^2 = a^2 + b^2$.

Prove: $\angle C$ is a rt. $\angle$.

Proof: Either $\angle C$ is acute, obtuse, or right.

If $\angle C$ is acute, then $c^2 = a^2 + b^2 - 2ab'$ which contradicts the hypothesis and therefore the assumption is false. If $\angle C$ is obtuse, then $c^2 = a^2 + b^2 + 2ab'$ which also contradicts the hypothesis. Therefore the remaining possibility that $\angle C$ is a right angle is true.

THEOREM 107. *The sum of the squares of any two sides of a triangle equals twice the square of one-half the third side plus twice the square of the median to that side.*

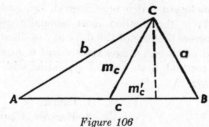

Figure 106

Prove that $a^2 + b^2 = 2\left(\dfrac{c}{2}\right)^2 + 2m^2$.

Proof: Apply Theorems 104 and 105, page 126 and add results.

THEOREM 108. *The sum of the squares of the diagonals of a parallelogram is equal to the sum of the squares of its four sides.*

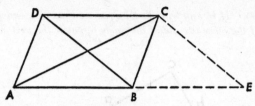

Figure 107

Prove: $\overline{AC}^2 + \overline{DB}^2 = \overline{AB}^2 + \overline{BC}^2 + \overline{CD}^2 + \overline{DA}^2$.

Proof: Draw $CE \parallel DB$. Extend AB to meet CE.

$$AB = DC = BE.$$

$$\therefore \overline{AC}^2 + \overline{CE}^2 = 2\overline{AB}^2 + 2\overline{BC}^2 \quad \text{(Theorem 107, page 127.)}$$

But $\qquad\qquad\qquad \overline{CE}^2 = \overline{DB}^2$

$$\therefore \overline{AC}^2 + \overline{DB}^2 = 2\overline{AB}^2 + 2\overline{BC}^2$$

or $\qquad\qquad \overline{AC}^2 + \overline{DB}^2 = \overline{AB}^2 + \overline{BC}^2 + \overline{CD}^2 + \overline{DA}^2$.

METHODS OF PROOF

The Synthetic Method. The synthetic method proceeds from the known to the unknown. It begins with the hypothesis and leads step by step to the conclusion. It is brief, logical, and leads directly to the desired result. It is the method most generally used in geometry textbooks. However, because of the difficulty of discovering each new step, this method often encourages the student to memorize the proof. In the synthetic method, if we have A given and wish to prove D, the steps are as follows:

1. A is true.   1. Given.
2. B is true.   2. Because A is true.
3. C is true.   3. Because A and B are true.
4. $\therefore D$ is true.   4. Because A, B, and C are true.

Geometric Illustration. If the diagonals of a quadrilateral bisect each other, the figure is a parallelogram.

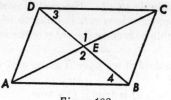

Figure 108

Proof:

1. $DE = EB$ and $CE = EA$.   1. Why?

2. $\angle 1 = \angle 2$ 2. Why?

3. $\triangle DEC \cong \triangle ABE$ 3. Why?

4. $\angle 3 = \angle 4$ and $DC = AB$ 4. Why?

5. $DC \parallel AB$ 5. Why?

6. $\therefore ABCD$ is a $\square$.   6. Why?

Algebraic Illustration. If $\dfrac{a}{b} = \dfrac{c}{d}$, then $\dfrac{a+b}{b} = \dfrac{c+d}{d}$.

Proof:

1. $\dfrac{a}{b} = \dfrac{c}{d}$.   1. Given

2. $\dfrac{a}{b} + 1 = \dfrac{c}{d} + 1$.   2. Why?

3. $\therefore \dfrac{a+b}{b} = \dfrac{c+d}{d}$.   3. Why?

EXERCISES

1. Prove by the synthetic method several of the exercises on pages 134–137.

2. If $\dfrac{a}{b} = \dfrac{c}{d}$, prove that $\dfrac{a^2}{b^2} = \dfrac{a^2 + c^2}{b^2 + d^2}$.

The Analytic Method. The analytic method proceeds from the unknown to the known. It begins with the conclusion and leads step by step back to the hypothesis. The analytic proof is longer and seems less direct. It makes it, however, much easier to discover each new step than in the synthetic proof. The analytic method is valuable in the discovery of a proof. However, in order to be sure that our proof is valid we must be able to reverse the order of the steps to the synthetic form.

In the analytic method, if we have *A* given and wish to prove *D*, the steps are as follows:

$$D \text{ is true if } C \text{ is true.}$$

$$C \text{ is true if } B \text{ is true.}$$

$$B \text{ is true if } A \text{ is true.}$$

But A is true. (Given) $\therefore D$ is true.

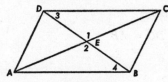

Figure 109

Geometric Illustration. If the diagonals of a quadrilateral bisect each other, the figure is a parallelogram.

Analysis:

1. $ABCD$ is a $\square$ if $DC = AB$ and if $DC \parallel AB$.

2. $DC \parallel AB$ if $\angle 3 = \angle 4$.

3. $\angle 3 = \angle 4$ and $DC \parallel AB$ if $\triangle DEC \cong \triangle ABE$.

4. $\triangle DEC \cong \triangle ABE$.

5. $\therefore ABCD$ may be proved a $\square$.

The proof having been discovered by the analytic method, the steps should now be reversed and it should be given in its synthetic form.

Algebraic Illustration.   If $\dfrac{a}{b} = \dfrac{c}{d}$, then $\dfrac{a+b}{b} = \dfrac{c+d}{d}$.

1. $\dfrac{a+b}{b} = \dfrac{c+d}{d}$ 1. This is true if 2 is true.

2. $ad + bd = bc + bd$.   2. This is true if 3 is true.

3. $ad = bc$.   3. This is true if 4 is true.

4. $\dfrac{a}{b} = \dfrac{c}{d}$. 　　　　　　4. But 4 is true by hypothesis.

　　　　　　　　　　　　　　∴ 1 is true.

EXERCISES

Use the analytical method in solving the following.

1. If $\dfrac{a}{b} = \dfrac{c}{d}$, prove that $\dfrac{a+b}{a-b} = \dfrac{c+d}{c-d}$.

2. If $\dfrac{a}{b} = \dfrac{c}{d}$, prove that $\dfrac{ab+b^2}{b^2} = \dfrac{cd^2+d^2}{d^2}$.

3. If the diagonals of a trapezoid meet in a trisection point of each, then one base of the trapezoid is twice the other.

The Indirect Proofs. The indirect proofs are not only valuable, but essential, for proving many of the theorems of geometry. Several types will be illustrated.

Illustration 1. In comparing two magnitudes of the same kind the first is either less than, equal to, or greater than the second. If we can show that two of these relationships are false, the third is true.

Example. If two angles of a triangle are unequal, the sides opposite these angles are unequal and the side opposite the greater angle is the greater.

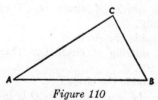

Figure 110

Given: $\triangle ABC$ with $\angle B > \angle A$.

Prove: $CA > CB$.

Proof:

1. $CA < CB$, or $CA = CB$, or $CA > CB$.
2. If $CA < CB$, then $\angle B < \angle A$. (Theorem 41, page 121.)
   But this is false for it contradicts the hypothesis.
3. If $CA = CB$, then $\angle B = \angle A$. (Theorem 3, page 119.)
   This is false for it contradicts the hypothesis.
4. ∴ $CA > CB$, for the other two possibilities have been excluded.

Illustration 2. The position of a point may sometimes be located by the indirect method as in the following:

A quadrilateral whose opposite angles are supplementary may be inscribed in a circle.

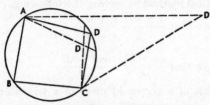

Figure 111

Given: Quadrilateral $ABCD$ with $\angle A + \angle C = 180°$; $\angle B + \angle D = 180°$.

Prove: $ABCD$ may be inscribed in a circle.

Proof:

1. A circle may be passed through the points A, B, and C.   All authorities left to the student.
2. The point D lies inside, on, or outside this circle.
3. Suppose D lies inside of circle O. Then $\angle B + \angle D > 180°$.
4. ∴ D cannot lie inside the circle.
5. Suppose D lies outside of circle O. Then $\angle B + \angle D < 180°$.
6. ∴ D cannot lie outside the circle.
7. ∴ D must lie on the circle and $ABCD$ is inscriptible in circle O.

Illustration 3. When a relationship has only two possibilities one of which must be true, a theorem may be proved by proving one of them false, as follows:

If two lines are cut by a transversal so that a pair of alternate interior angles are equal, the lines are parallel.

In this case the lines are parallel or they are not parallel. We **may** prove the lines parallel by proving the opposite false.

Proof: Consult an elementary text.

EXERCISES
(Use an indirect method)

1. Consult an elementary geometry text and list the theorems proved by the indirect method.

2. If $\begin{cases} \text{when } a = b, \ x = y \\ \text{when } a > b, \ x > y \\ \text{when } a < b, \ x < y \end{cases}$, then each converse is true.

Prove that the converse of each of the above facts is true. This is known as the Law of Converses.

3. The shortest line that can be drawn from a point to a line is the perpendicular.

4. If two angles of a triangle are equal, the sides opposite these angles are equal.

5. A right angle is inscriptible in a semicircle.

6. Two lines parallel to the same line are parallel to each other.

7. If two parallel lines are cut by a transversal, the alternate interior angles are equal.

8. State and prove the converse of: If two chords of a circle are unequal, the greater is nearer the center.

9. If the median to one side of a triangle is not perpendicular to it the other two sides are not equal.

10. If an isosceles triangle and a scalene triangle are constructed on a common base, the line joining their vertices does not bisect the base.

11. If the square on one side of a triangle is less than the sum of the squares of the other two sides, the angle opposite the first side is acute.

12. If a line cuts one of two parallel lines it must cut the other.

13. Lines perpendicular to two intersecting lines also intersect.

14. A point unequally distant from the ends of a line segment is not on the perpendicular bisector of the segment.

15. The bisectors of two angles of a triangle intersect.

Suggestions for Solving Exercises. The ability to solve exercises is of fundamental importance to the prospective teacher. It depends upon a knowledge of the methods to be used and a certain ingenuity in their use. Fortunately there is no general plan which will assure success, since this would destroy much of the pleasure derived. However, the following suggestions will be of value.

1. Study the exercise for a clear interpretation and pick out the hypothesis and conclusion.

2. Draw an accurate general figure marking the hypothesis. Remember the entire hypothesis should be used.
3. Recall the various methods for proving the desired relationship and choose the most probable one.
4. If no method applies directly use analysis marking equal parts and supplying needed construction lines.
5. Sometimes the indirect method of proof is easier than the direct method.
6. A solution is often obtained by using algebra.

EXERCISES

1. If through any point on a diagonal of a parallelogram parallels to the sides are drawn, the parallelograms on opposite sides of that diagonal are equal in area.
2. The lines joining the midpoints of the adjacent sides of any quadrilateral form a parallelogram whose area is equal to half the area of the quadrilateral.
3. The medians from the vertices of the equal angles of an isosceles triangle are equal.
4. If the opposite angles of a quadrilateral are equal, the figure is a parallelogram.
5. The lines drawn from two opposite vertices of a parallelogram to the midpoints of the opposite sides trisect the diagonal joining the other two vertices.
6. The base angles of an isosceles trapezoid are equal.
7. If two equal (in area) triangles are drawn on the opposite sides of a common base, the line joining their vertices is bisected by the common base, or by the base produced.
8. If the base angles of a trapezoid are equal, it is isosceles.
9. An exterior angle at the base of an isosceles triangle is equal to 90° plus half the vertex angle.
10. If equilateral triangles are drawn on the three sides of any triangle and lying outside the given triangle, the lines joining their vertices with the opposite vertices of the given triangle are equal.
11. The lines joining the midpoints of the opposite sides of a quadrilateral bisect each other.
12. If from any point on the base of an isosceles triangle perpendiculars are drawn to the two equal sides, their sum is equal to the altitude drawn from one of the equal angles.

13. The angle formed by the bisectors of any two consecutive angles of a quadrilateral is equal to half the sum of the other two angles.

14. The line joining the midpoints of the legs of a trapezoid is equal to half the sum of the bases.

15. If perpendiculars are drawn from any point within an equilateral triangle to the sides, their sum equals an altitude of the triangle.

16. The line joining the midpoints of two opposite sides of a quadrilateral bisects the line joining the midpoints of the diagonals.

17. The sum of the perpendiculars from any point in the base of an isosceles triangle to the equal sides is constant.

18. The line joining the midpoints of the diagonals of a trapezoid is equal to half the difference of the bases.

19. If through the point of intersection of the diagonals of any parallelogram two lines are drawn connecting the pairs of opposite sides, and their ends are joined consecutively, a new parallelogram is formed.

20. If the diagonals of a trapezoid are equal, the trapezoid is isosceles.

21. The shortest chord that can be drawn through a point within a circle is the perpendicular to the radius through that point.

22. Circles are described on the three sides of a right triangle as diameters. Prove that the area of the one on the hypotenuse is equal to the sum of the areas of the other two.

23. Find the radius of a circle in which the area is numerically equal to the radius.

24. Three equal circles of diameter 1 are drawn so that each is tangent to the other two. Find the area inclosed by the three arcs between the points of tangency.

25. The common chord of two circles if produced bisects the segment of their common tangent between its points of contact.

26. If two circles intersect, prove that any two parallel lines drawn through their points of intersection and terminated by the respective circles are equal.

27. Given two circles tangent externally at P, and MN a common tangent with M and N the points of contact. Prove the angle MPN a right angle.

28. If from any point P two equal tangents PB and PC are drawn to two circles O and O', and PD is perpendicular to OO' then $\overline{OB}^2 - \overline{O'C}^2 = \overline{OD}^2 - \overline{O'D}^2$.

29. A side of a circumscribed equilateral triangle is twice that of the side of an equilateral triangle inscribed in the same circle.

30. Of all triangles having a common base and equal altitudes, the isosceles triangle has the greatest vertical angle.

31. The lines joining the midpoints of the sides of a triangle form a triangle similar to the given triangle.

32. If a parallelogram is not a rectangle, its diagonals are unequal.

33. Prove that a point not in the perpendicular bisector of a line is unequally distant from the ends of the line.

34. Any point within an angle and not on its bisector is unequally distant from the sides of the angle. (Use both the direct and indirect methods.)

35. If a line is drawn through one of the points of intersection of two equal circles, its extremeties on the circles are equidistant from the other point of intersection.

36. If two unequal chords of a circle are produced to meet, the secants thus formed are unequal and the one nearer the center of the circle is the greater.

37. If the bisector of an inscribed angle is extended to meet the circle and through this point of intersection a chord is drawn parallel to one side of the angle, it will equal the other side.

38. Derive the formula for the area of an equilateral triangle whose side is s.

39. Derive the formula for the median of a triangle in terms of its sides.

40. If the square on one side of a triangle is greater than the sum of the squares on the other two sides, the triangle is obtuse.

41. If two circles are tangent externally and through the point of contact a secant is drawn, the chords cut on it are proportional to the radii of the circles.

42. The square on the side of a triangle opposite a sixty degree angle equals the sum of the squares on the other two sides less their product.

43. Find the number of sides of a polygon if the sum of its interior angles exceeds the sum of its exterior angles by 2340°.

44. What part of the area of a triangle is the area of the quadrilateral formed by drawing two medians?

45. The area of a trapezoid is equal to the product of a leg and the perpendicular drawn to it (extended if necessary) from the midpoint of the other leg.

46. The area of a regular inscribed hexagon is the mean proportional between the areas of the circumscribed and inscribed regular triangles.

47. The projections of two parallel sides of a parallelogram upon the other two sides are equal.

48. Two triangles are equal in area if two sides of one are equal to two sides of the other and their included angles are supplementary.

49. Find the area of a circle inscribed in an equilateral triangle whose area is $36\sqrt{3}$ sq. in.

50. If in the triangle ABC the altitudes AD and BE intersect in F, then $BF \times BE = BC \times BD$.

Suggestions for Solving Problems.   If a problem cannot be solved by putting together the given parts or by the use of a simple construction line, analysis should be used.

1. Make a diagram of the construction as it will appear when completed.

2. Mark on the diagram all given parts or those that are determined from the given parts.

3. Find some part of the figure (usually a triangle) which can be constructed and make this the starting point for the construction.

4. If no determined triangle can be found, draw additional construction lines.

5. Complete the construction and prove that it satisfies the given conditions.

6. Explain whether the construction is always possible and indicate the possible number of solutions.

Example.   Construct a triangle, given two sides and the median to the third side.

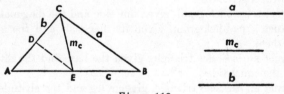

Figure 112

Analysis: Since no triangle is determined in the diagram we draw ED parallel to a. ED equals $\frac{1}{2}a$ and bisects b.   Thus the triangle DEC is determined.

Construction: Construct a triangle with $\frac{1}{2}b$, $\frac{1}{2}a$, and m_c as sides and from this complete the construction.

The solution of a problem may depend upon the drawing of construction lines. The following are the common conditions for such lines.

1. Through or connecting two points.
2. Through a given point and parallel to a given line.
3. Through a given point and perpendicular to a given line.
4. Bisecting a given angle.
5. A line making a given angle with a given line
6. The extension of a given line segment.
7. Laying off a line equal to a given line.

Example: Through a given point construct a line which will form equal angles with the sides of a given angle.

First, bisect the given angle and then construct a perpendicular from the given point to the bisector of the angle and extend it to the sides of the angle. Prove the two triangles thus formed are congruent.

Lettering the Triangle. The parts of a triangle will be denoted as follows: The sides a, b, and c, are opposite respectively angles A, B, and C. The altitudes to a, b, and c are lettered h_a, h_b, and h_c respectively the medians to a, b, and c are m_a, m_b, and m_c, and the bisectors, of A, B, and C, are t_a, t_b, and t_c.

PROBLEMS

1. Construct a triangle, given C, B, and h_a.
2. Construct a triangle, given a, b, m_b.
3. Through a given point construct a line which will make a given angle with a given line.
4. Construct a parallelogram, given one side and the diagonals.
5. Construct a parallelogram, given its diagonals and the angle between them.
6. Construct an isosceles triangle, given the base and the altitude to one of the equal sides.
7. Construct an isosceles triangle, given a leg and the altitude to that leg.
8. Construct an isosceles trapezoid, given the bases and one base angle.
9. Through a given point draw a line cutting two parallel lines so that a segment of given length is intercepted by the parallels.
10. Construct a triangle, given the midpoints of its sides.
11. Construct an isosceles triangle, given the base and the vertical angle.

12. Construct a triangle, given A, B, and $a + c$.
13. Construct a right triangle, given the hypotenuse and the sum of the other sides.
14. Construct a trapezoid, given the four sides.
15. Trisect a right angle.
16. Construct an angle of $7\frac{1}{2}°$.
17. Given a line segment AB.   Construct a line segment which will equal $\sqrt{2}\ AB$, $\sqrt{3}\ AB$.
18. Construct a square, given the sum of a diagonal and a side.
19. Through a given point draw a line which will be equally distant from two given points.
20. Construct a triangle, given the perimeter and two angles.
21. Through a given point within a circle construct the shortest possible chord.
22. Draw the shortest line that can be drawn from an external point to a circle.
23. Through a given point within a circle draw a chord that will be bisected by the point.
24. Draw the shortest line that can be drawn from an internal point to a circle.
25. Through a given external point to draw a secant from which the circle will cut a chord equal to a given chord.
26. Draw a line tangent to a circle and parallel to a given line.
27. Draw a circle having a given radius and tangent to two given circles.
28. Draw a circle having a given radius and tangent to two intersecting lines.
29. Draw a circle having a given radius that will pass through a given point and be tangent to a given line.
30. Through a given point of a chord draw another chord which will equal it.
31. Draw a line cutting chords of given lengths from two circles.
32. Inscribe a square in a semicircle.
33. Inscribe a square in a triangle.
34. On the base of a given triangle construct a triangle equal in area to the given triangle and having its vertex on a given line.
35. Construct on a given base a rectangle equal in area to a given square.
36. Construct a square equal in area to a given triangle.
37. Construct a square equal in area to one-half of a given square.
38. Draw a line through one side of a triangle which will cut off a triangle similar to the given triangle and equal to one-half of it.

39. Draw a line through the vertex of a triangle dividing it into two parts having a ratio of m to n.
40. Through a point without a parallelogram draw a line which will divide it into two equivalent parts.
41. Divide a line segment into parts having the ratio of 1 to $\sqrt{2}$.
42. Construct a triangle given a, b, $(b:c)$.
43. Construct a right isosceles triangle equivalent to a given triangle.
44. From a point without a circle draw a secant which will be bisected by the circle.
45. Construct a triangle, given m_b, h_b, m_c.
46. Construct a triangle, given the base, the sum of the other two sides, and the angle included by them.
47. Construct a right triangle, given a leg and the altitude to the hypotenuse.
48. Find a point on one side of a triangle which is equidistant from the other two vertices.
49. Through a given point draw a line which will make equal angles with two given lines.
50. Through a given point on a circle draw a chord that is bisected by a given chord.

Index